Ex Líbrís

PRACTICAL
MILK PRODUCTION

PRACTICAL MILK PRODUCTION

DAVID W. MORRIS
B Sc (Wales), PhD (Dunelm), FRAgS

FARMING PRESS LIMITED
FENTON HOUSE, WHARFEDALE ROAD, IPSWICH, SUFFOLK

First published 1976

ISBN 0 85236 058 4

*Set in ten on eleven point Times and printed in Great Britain on Paladin Cartridge
paper by The Leagrave Press Limited, Luton and London, for Farming Press
Limited.*

CONTENTS

5

ILLUSTRATIONS

PHOTOGRAPHS

DIAGRAMS

FOREWORD

By M. M. COOPER
*Formerly Dean of Agriculture, Newcastle upon Tyne, and
Chief Research Co-ordinator, World Bank Project for
Research and Development in Agriculture, Spain.*

THIS BOOK HAS been published at a very critical stage of the British dairy industry, which, with its contribution to meat supplies, accounts for approximately 30 per cent of the gross value of agricultural production. For many decades it has been an expanding industry and the sheet anchor of our farming, but recently it has gone into decline with a significant reduction not only in the number of herds and of cows in milk, but also in the number of heifers reared as herd replacements.

The factors contributing to this are diverse, but the principal reason unquestionably is that rapid rises in the costs of production have not been adequately offset by increased farm-gate prices for milk. It seems that our political masters are more concerned with the short-term benefit of providing housewives with cheap milk than with the long-term stability of a branch of farming that is so important, both dietetically and economically, to the welfare of this country. At the time of writing this Foreword, we have a ridiculous situation where the cost of posting a letter is as great as that of a pint of milk, while a pint of beer at the local costs three times more than a pint of milk delivered to the door.

If this decline is to be reversed, and the industry is to realise in a greater measure its biological potential for milk production to the point of a much greater degree of self-sufficiency for milk and milk products than the present 60 per cent, in order to lessen our chronic balance of payments problems there is no doubt that dairy farmers must have a fair crack of the whip. This does not infer, however, that the problems of the industry will be resolved solely by substantial price increments, for there must also be improvements in economic efficiency. This is not a novel concept because one of the outstanding features of post-war agriculture has been the enormous increase in the technical and economic efficiency of our dairy industry, which in almost every respect compares more than favourably with that of every other country in the Community, with the possible exception of the Netherlands. Great as the progress has been in the past, there can be no grounds for complacency, particularly in respect of the production and utilisation of grassland where the performance of the average dairy farmer leaves much to be desired. One has only to look at the results that the best of our dairy farmers achieve to see the scope there is for improvement and for reducing the reliance on imported feedingstuffs.

It is in this respect that the publication of this book is of such great importance. It analyses effectively all the factors that contribute to the vast complex that is efficient dairying, based on a fuller realisation of a grassland potential greater than that of any other country of Western Europe—with the possible exception of Ireland, whose farmers could, with profit to themselves, take heed of the lessons of this book.

Dr Morris is no theoretician. Before his present appointment he was a highly successful farm manager, and the remarkable success of the College's Frondeg herd, established only five years ago, is very much to his credit. It is the outcome of applying the principles that he elaborates in this book. He is one of the few College principals in Britain who could in an emergency take over from his cowman and not only do this competently, but with all the pleasure that a true stockman derives from working with animals. Unquestionably this book is a major contribution to the future welfare of this country's dairy industry and it comes from a man still well on the right side of forty, who has the widely acknowledged reputation of being one of the outstanding authorities on grassland dairy farming.

M. M. Cooper

Holme House,
Lesbury,
Northumberland
October, 1975

PREFACE

WHEN THIS BOOK was first considered in the autumn of 1973, it was difficult to foresee what would happen to milk production in the next few years. Publishing was delayed to allow for the changes, particularly costs, to settle down, but I am afraid that even now, with the dilemma of joining the European Economic Community now resolved, there are still a very large number of uncertainties facing the dairy industry. I would need a very clear crystal ball to look even a short distance into the future and I have tried as far as possible not to quote current costs and returns, as they will, in all probability, be out of date by the time this book is read.

The June 1975 Ministry of Agriculture returns showed a marked decrease in dairy cow numbers. Compared with June 1973, there was in June 1975 a total fall of 233,000 dairy cows in milk; dairy cows in calf and dairy heifers in calf for the first time, a drop of 6·8 per cent in two years. Individual herd sizes are increasing, but this is not sufficient to compensate for the number of farms giving up milk production.

In future, a very large proportion of milk-producing farms will be family farms, with herds of 80–120 cows managed by one man with help from a relief milker. Family farms of this size will be extremely important, as family labour, with a deep interest in the job, will be the mainstay of production. There will of course be larger herds but I do not like to see herds grow above the 150-cow size, as problems of handling, feeding, etc become far greater after this, as well as a definite increase in cow stress, particularly for weaker members of the herd.

It is regrettable that increase in unit size in all branches of agriculture makes it more and more difficult for young men to enter the industry as farmers. It may well be feasible to develop a 'share-milking' system similar to the system in New Zealand, whereby a young man can, by hard work, build up his own herd. On larger farms this may well be one of the ways of solving the acute shortage of good herdsmen, as the incentive for the share milker in owning or part-owning his herd will be great.

Milk prices have crept up very slowly in the last two years, particularly in relation to increases in costs. A very modest return on tenant's capital, which invariably means a very small return on total capital involved, cannot be tolerated and unless put right, we will see more and more producers discontinuing milk production. Unfortunately, milk features (with potatoes) in the calculation of the food price index, and there is therefore a reluctance on the part of successive governments to increase doorstep prices. It is inevitable in the near future, to provide a just return and cash for expansion, that the present ridiculously low rate of doorstep prices must be doubled.

Expansion is necessary to provide for the increasing liquid market. There should also be a planned system for the manufacture of milk products. This would result in an enormous saving of imports of cheese, butter and other milk products, and would be received with delight by the rest of the EEC countries who now subsidise dairy imports into this country.

There has been great technical progress made in milk production in this country. The Milk Marketing Board's breeding policy has improved the National herd dramatically. Let us hope that these technical advances can be matched by a healthy, profitable market to the farmer for his milk.

I would like to thank everyone who has helped with the preparation of this book. To my stepfather, Mr E J Lewis, who first aroused my interest in breeding better high-producing dairy cows, and Professor Mac Cooper at Cockle Park for teaching me in his inimitable way the close relationship between good grassland husbandry and animal production.

Mrs Beryl Morgan, my secretary, deserves a very special mention and a 'Thank you' for her patience and expertise in not only deciphering my scrawl, but also for her invaluable assistance in putting this book together.

I also thank Mr Alan Leather, Mr John Saycell, and Mrs Margaret Whiteman and her staff for help with photographs, diagrams and indexing.

I have been fortunate in starting a new herd at Frondeg. Many people have helped with its development, but without the expertise and hard work of the herdsman, Mr Don Schofield, I would have no worthwhile results to quote.

Lastly, I am most grateful to my wife Cynthia, who has not only tolerated long periods of disruption to our family life while this book was written, but has been invaluable to me for her constructive criticism and opinion. Her continued interest and patience has helped greatly in the production of this book.

DAVID MORRIS

Llanbadarn Fawr,
Aberystwyth
August, 1975

Chapter 1

INTRODUCTION

IT IS DIFFICULT to imagine that less than one hundred years ago the milk-producing industry as it is known today was in its infancy. Our large cities were rapidly expanding at that time, and as there was no efficient transport system, no refrigeration, or even facilities to produce clean milk as we know it today, most of the milk was produced from herds housed in the cities themselves. In London, for example, in 1850 there were an estimated 26,000 cows, bought in calf from a large area outside the city and kept strictly as a flying herd, that is, milked for one lactation only and then sold to the butcher.

Most of the city herds were maintained in byres, fed a ration of hay, which was apparently easier to transport from the perimeter of the city than milk, and also brewers' grains. Little is known of their method of manure disposal, but it is obvious that handling manure in dairy units is not as modern a problem as it would seem by the recent attention it has attracted.

The town milk supplier must have obviously worked very hard indeed, not only being involved in hand-milking the herd, often three times a day to extract the highest yield possible, but also in tending the cows and delivering the milk. Many of these dairymen were from the west, and particularly mid-Wales. Natives of Cardiganshire were well known in London as milkmen for a very long time. It was traditional for many years for at least one member of a mid-Wales family, and in particular a Cardiganshire farming family, to join the milk trade in London. Many returned to Wales to 'retire' at quite a young age, and were responsible for building large houses on their return, which can be taken to indicate that their hard work had not been in vain financially!

During the 1850s and into the 1860s, there were dramatic changes in milk transportation. This was the era of the development of a very comprehensive railway system, which eased the problem of the transportation of milk not only to cities, but also to rapidly growing industrial areas.

Milk produced in outlying farms or areas of low population, and with no outlet as fresh milk, was made into butter or cheese on the farm and then transported to towns and cities for sale.

In the early 1850s an estimated total of three million cows, produced 750 million gallons (3,410 million litres) per year, but as yet the contribution of milk to the diet of the nation was quite small. It is also interesting to note that, at that time, the average lactation was only 250 gallons (1,140 litres). Ironically, as will be discussed later, the milk-producing industry has relied on hardships and war to supply it with impetus to expand. In 1865 and 1866 these city herds were almost totally destroyed by cattle plague, which together with the concurrent development of the railway system, meant that city dairy-men became purely retailers of milk in the main, relying on their supply being delivered by rail from a wide area. Some town dairies remained, and even today (1975), it is reported that 22 milk producers remain within the Greater London boundary.

During the years that followed, demand for milk, butter and cheese grew rapidly. These were the years of the Great Depression, and it was a highly important fact for the smaller producers that milk production, particularly around cities, remained reasonably profitable.

MAJOR BRANCH OF AGRICULTURE

In 1876 the first London Dairy Show was held, and the British Dairy Farmers' Association was formed at that show. Dairying was about to emerge at this time as a major branch of agriculture. Many breed societies were formed during this period, with of course the Shorthorn being the main breed at that time. In 1870 there was another significant development, the establishment of the first cheese factory followed rapidly by many others.

During the 1890s milk wholesalers grew in number and size very rapidly to deal with the marketing of milk. These wholesalers undertook a very important role, forming the link between producers and consumer. Milk from farms was originally delivered by the farmer to the country station, or alternatively in some areas, to newly-built milk processing factories.

Milking was as yet carried out entirely by hand, and very often by women. In 1969, on Pinhills farm, on the Marquis of Lansdowne's Bowood Estate in Wiltshire, which I managed, we milked 150 cows, and we thought that this was, (and quite rightly) big business, only to realise on reading the records that around 100 cows were milked on the same farm in 1890 by 20 women from neighbouring Calne.

It is known that a milking machine patent was taken out in 1849 in the United States. It was not until the early years of the twentieth century that a successful machine became available for commercial use in this country, resulting of course in a gradual decrease in the labour demand for milking.

During the relatively short time from 1900 to 1930 further great progress was made but not always, regrettably, in the right direction. Dairy companies became large and prosperous but, unfortunately, often at the expense of the primary producer. Half-yearly contracts were often broken or not renewed, and prices paid were very often too low. During this period, however, there was a great deal of progress in the method of production, and the maintenance of clean fresh milk, free of harmful organisms.

The larger dairy companies, with their adequate resources, were able to afford pasteurising, followed later by bottling plants, which was a great step forward from the previous 'churn to jug' distribution system. But it was not until 1923 with the passing of the first Milk (Special Designation) Order, that quality grades, and even pasteurisation, were given official recognition.

RAPID PROGRESS IN MILK INDUSTRY

The First World War, and the period immediately afterwards, was a time when the milk industry progressed rapidly. The development of road haulage to supplement and service the existing railway network opened up many more areas, giving easier access to the milk factories. In 1920 the National Milk Publicity Council was formed, followed by the 1921 Education Acts providing for school milk schemes, a scheme that was to continue successfully for 50 years. This undoubtedly did more good towards educating young people to drink fresh milk than any other scheme ever devised.

During this time, there is no doubt that drinking fresh milk from infected cows caused the spread of tuberculosis on a very wide scale. Pasteurisation helped to control this in areas of denser population. This service was not available to country people, who still drank untreated milk direct from the farm or sold by small village suppliers. The Tuberculosis Order of 1925 and the Milk and Dairies Order of 1926 were important, but it was the Attested Herds Scheme of 1934 that was without doubt the most important scheme. It was 26 years later, in 1960, that the whole country achieved tuberculin attestation of all cows.

While progress had steadily been made in the production, health and distribution of milk, marketing was still far from satisfactory. In 1932 a serious attempt was made to improve marketing by the formation of the Permanent Joint Milk Committee, whose terms of reference were to regulate prices, by collective bargaining between producers (the weak ones) and the buyers (the strong ones) who were by then almost in complete control. There was no legal backing given to this Committee's suggested actions, and the position, whereby producers were being exploited, changed very little.

The situation was so bad that it led to the formation of the Milk Marketing Board in 1933. This has become the most successful body to organise the marketing of milk, or indeed any other agricultural product on a national level in the whole world, as well as of course being responsible for the development of its many ancillary services, recording, artificial breeding schemes, and costing services for the dairy farmer.

This move to form the Milk Marketing Board was most significant in that farmer/producers waived their freedom to market their product individually and placed total reliance and trust in the control of prices and conditions of sale in their elected Board. The Board, from then on, became a far more powerful body to deal with the already existing band of milk retailing and processing companies. In one move the position of the producers, acting together, changed from being very weak, to being very strong.

It was not until the Second World War that the value of milk as a food was appreciated fully, and demand became so great that it resulted in controls being exercised in the form of near rationing. This demand for liquid milk virtually stopped the production of farmhouse butter and cheese, at least officially. The function of the Milk Marketing Board as a negotiating body came to a temporary halt, being replaced by compulsory powers in the control of the Ministry of Food.

It was not until 1954 that the Board was partially returned to its functions, but even to this day (1975) the Minister of Agriculture, Fisheries and Food fixes producer prices and the retail price of milk, together with payment schemes that are designed to control the level of milk production on a national scale, although not always successfully!

BRUCELLOSIS ERADICATION SCHEMES

Payment on compositional and hygienic quality has progressed, particularly in the last few years. Nearly all milk now sold retail to the public is heat-treated and safe to drink, and the long overdue Brucellosis Eradication Schemes are well under way. I am fortunate to live in a 'clean area' and hope that the eradication of this dreaded disease of both cattle and humans will not take 26 years as did the eradication of tuberculosis.

Currently (1975), England and Wales has 2·82 million dairy cows, Scotland has 319,000 and Northern Ireland has a further 239,000. Annual average yields per cow are now 895 gallons (4,072 litres) compared with 250 gallons (1,140 litres) as mentioned earlier in 1850. The total average daily production in the United Kingdom is now a staggering 2,928 million gallons (13,315 million litres) and when one considers that only 100 years ago with no refrigeration, pasteurisation plants, etc, the dairy industry was slowly emerging.

The recognition of milk as a cheap wholesome food is still progressing, partly due to the Milk Marketing Board's publicity campaigns. In 1972 every man, woman and child in England and Wales drank 325 pints (184 litres) of milk during the year. This figure has remained constant over the last 20 years. This is despite short-sighted government policies of discontinuing free milk in schools after the childrens' seventh birthday, and consequently the ever-present likelihood of breaking this habit of drinking milk through the rest of their lives. When we consider the price of a pint of beer at 24p, however much we may enjoy it, to the price of milk currently (1975) at $8\frac{1}{2}$p per pint, we realise the value of milk to the general public.

It is as well, in an introductory chapter, to discuss milk production, and to remember that we are dependent on a market, preferably an expanding one, and it is through the hard work of the producers themselves, coupled with that of the Milk Marketing Board's, that an increase in milk consumption and an increase in sales off farms has been possible. If the liquid market had not expanded, this would have dramatically affected our price ex farm received, as milk sold to manufacture, particularly for buttermaking, realises a far lower price than that sold as liquid milk. Without this market, discussions on housing, feeding, breeding, etc in later chapters would have been completely irrelevant.

Joining the European Economic Community as full members will of course bring changes, but let us hope as producers, and as a heavy milk-consuming nation, that our milk industry will be safeguarded. Overproduction will be disastrous, even though increasing the dairy herd to provide calves for beef production has been given as a constant reason for the dairy herd's expansion. The continuation of a healthy and increasing demand for milk is essential for our expansion. We must guard our outlet to the consumer carefully, and always remember that as yet the average consumption in the United Kingdom, as mentioned earlier, is 325 pints (184 litres) per annum, compared with only 141 pints (80 litres) in the whole of the rest of the EEC countries.

Chapter 2

THE BREED STRUCTURE

I MAKE NO apology for being biased towards the Friesian breed. Ever since I can remember, I was involved with them and got to know the breed.

My career has, however, attempted to correct this bias, particularly during the period I was managing the Cockle Park Jerseys in Northumberland, where I learnt that, purely as convertors of grass into milk fat and solids, the Jersey was possibly as efficient as any breed. Later, as manager of Bowood Estate in Wiltshire, I was confronted with 300 Ayrshire milkers, and although I have always admired the breed for its excellent udder shape, its teat placings, and handsome carriage, I am afraid I was 'guilty' of top crossing every cow on the estate with Friesian semen.

Probably my only justification for this bias is that thousands of other dairy farmers have gone the same way, and even on a recent visit to New Zealand—the second home of the Jersey—I was to find that in 1973, 65 per cent of all dairy cow inseminations, mostly Jerseys, were by a Friesian bull. It is little wonder that when I had the comparatively rare opportunity of founding a new herd at the Welsh Agricultural College, that pedigree Friesians were chosen.

The development of the Friesian cow has no doubt contributed to the development of dairying in Britain from the turn of the century. It is obvious from photographs of that time that British breeders have improved the breed tremendously.

Commercially important points, 'wearability' of the udder, teat size and placings, have improved. I am not too sure, however, if the wearability of feet and legs has improved, or how much of today's feet trouble is due to our methods of housing and management.

There is still a long way to go, particularly with the width of the fore udder, a point I am particularly keen on, especially when putting on teat cups and hearing all sorts of sucking and whistling noises from older cows with teats set at twenty-to-four.

Production standards have of course also improved. In 1954/55 average yields of recorded Friesian herds was 948 gallons (4,310 litres) at 3·54 per cent butterfat. In 1973/74 it had increased to 1,046 gallons (4,755 litres) at 3·68 per cent butterfat. The introduction of the modern Dutch cow has done much to improve butterfat, and the emergence of the medium-sized, deep-bodied, straight-legged British Friesian cow has been a gradual and very interesting development.

More recently, the 'import anything on four legs' fever that has infected this country has meant widespread use of Canadian Holsteins. I am very sceptical of this development, as with a fully developed sophisticated artificial insemination system, untold damage could be done to any breed by the use of untested bulls on a very large scale for no other reason than to follow a current trend, in a similar way to ladies donning quite unsuitable clothes merely to keep up with fashion.

There is no doubt that some of these Canadian Holsteins have a high milk potential, but one must remember that in their native country, these cows are used to feeding regimes, not based on relatively cheap grass and grass products, and are from smaller herds fed excellent maize silage, lucerne hay and a lot of concentrates.

It is my view, particularly because of weak legs, and 'heely' feet, we will quickly return to our former problems, and that these importations are merely a passing phase, and many breeders will regret having produced these long-legged giants with a maintenance requirement, and corresponding appetite, 30 per cent higher than our own Friesian cow.

I always maintain that a breed discussion very often becomes an irrational argument and should be avoided in the same way as a discussion on politics or religion. This is true with students, and equally with farmers, but it is as well to remember that all breeds have their good and bad points and the keen man with his chosen breed, whatever it may be, will make a go of it.

WHEN COMPARING BREEDS

When comparing breeds, and production between herds of the same breed, we must always be very careful to remember exactly what one is comparing. This will be discussed in later chapters, but to compare a 900-gallon (4,095-litre) cow or herd with a 1,200-gallon (5,460-litre) cow or herd, is of no value unless one also knows the management of these animals and particularly feed input. A 900-gallon (4,095-litre) spring-calving cow, being fed 11 cwt (560 kg) of concentrates consisting mostly of rolled barley, may well compare favourably in terms of potential with a 1,500 gallon (6,825 litre) autumn-calving cow, fed upwards of two tons (2,032 kg) of concentrates. Similarly, a Jersey cow of 800 lb (363 kg) liveweight and yielding 700 gallons (3,185 litres) per year may well be as efficient or even more so than a 1,200 gallon (5,460 litre) Friesian cow weighing 1,400 lb (635 kg) at calving.

Many dairy farmers will still tend to choose bulls from fashionable herds with high yields and usually a correspondingly high concentrate usage. These production standards are almost certainly due to management expertise and feed, and the genetic potential of the herd in fact may be no greater than their own. Often, the selection of a bull calf from their own top-yielding cow, known to be superior *under their own conditions* may well be a better bet for them.

Pedigree breeders, however, are quite justified in saying that their business of producing bulls is a commercial proposition, admittedly under high cost conditions, and that while farmers will come to them to buy these bulls, they will offer this service.

I am not in any way decrying the service that pedigree breeders have contributed towards improving our breeds and production standards. Prefixes such as Grove, Hunday, Terling and Lavenham and Normead, to name but a few in the Friesian world, have contributed immensely to breed improvement in commercial herds in which a large proportion of their bulls, particularly through AI are used. If they had nothing to offer, they would not have succeeded as they have got to pay their way just like any other farmer, and it is as well to remember that few geneticists have produced an influence in cattle breeding comparable to those named.

WHEN CHOOSING A BULL

One point over which I have a quarrel with the Milk Marketing Board and commercial breeding companies is that, when choosing a bull, no one can tell me what bull should be used for a particular management system. With our spring-calving herd, one is aware of the autumn-calving situation. A bull with a national contemporary comparison of +50 gallons (+227·3 litres) that is known to produce daughters well above average for milk production may, however, not produce daughters in our specifically spring calving herd with a similar weighting. One +60 gallon (+273 litre) bull we have used has given us a consistently minus comparison with his contemporaries, as his daughters are large and lean and do not have the reserve to maintain yields on an all-grass diet, while smaller contemporaries have consistently outyielded them.

I will not name the bull in question, but needless to say his ancestors experienced more winter snow than we do in Britain.

This book is not about beef, but it would be wrong not to mention the dairy bull calf. Beef production in Britain is dependent to a very large extent on the bull calf from the dairy herd. By sheer weight of numbers the Friesian bull calf is important, and when we realised its potential for growth back in the 50's, it has progressively become more popular. Two systems, the semi-intensive 18-month beef system with autumn born calves, and then the more recent 24-month beef system with spring born calves, have taught us how to use these calves. Intensive or barley beef depends on the three conditions: price of calf, price of barley and the selling price.

The crossbred calf from the Friesian needs no great attention here, and the Hereford cross, both as a grass-fattening animal or a very good breeding female, has been extremely valuable. More recently, the larger Continental crosses have become more evident, but great care has to be taken to avoid calving difficulties which may wipe out completely any advantage in calf value. Calving difficulties may result in a dead calf, or worse still a dead cow.

INTRODUCTION OF CHAROLAIS

The introduction of the Charolais in particular has resulted in very useful beef crosses being produced from other breeds. At Cockle Park the little Jersey covered with a Charolais has produced very acceptable beef calves, and the females are very good and handsome breeding cows. Nearby, the Howie brothers in Acklington produce excellent cattle by inseminating the lower producers in their very good Ayrshire herd with Charolais semen.

The value of the bull calf from the dairy cow will vary with current beef prices. Even very recently (July 1975) we have seen prices range from £40 to £50 for a reasonable Friesian bull calf and £60 to £70 for a Charolais cross to prices so low that one is loath to quote, only hoping that when this book reaches publication, prices will have recovered to a reasonable level. A good price for a surplus bull calf is invaluable for the milk producer, adding considerably to his income at relatively low cost. It is a sad fact, however, that when calf prices are low, cull cow prices are also low, thereby reducing substantially the income from the dairy herd.

Chapter 3

THE CALF

WHEN DISCUSSING CALVES we must not be led astray by their continually fluctuating values. In most individual dairy herds, and of course in the general structure of the national dairy herd, calves, and indeed all young dairy stock, are integral and important parts of the dairying system. The efficiency of the succeeding generation is dependent on the quality of the herd's young stock and this can be modified by the method of rearing employed.

The newly dropped heifer calf is a valuable asset to the herd. Losses may mean that, to maintain herd numbers, heifers or cows may have to be bought in. This is an exercise that is not only subject to considerable risk, but also demands the finding of ready cash to finance the operation, as compared with the introduction of one's own heifers, whose costs, although considerable, have been absorbed to a considerable extent on the farm. I will not discuss here the pros and cons of rearing or not rearing one's own replacements, but merely state that often the farmer who survives longest in a financial crisis is the man who pays out the least number of cheques.

Calving problems feature very much in a farmer's or herdsman's mind, and thankfully this breed of men has an inbuilt knowledge and willingness to get up at all hours of the night, a factor that must be responsible for saving the lives of thousands of calves per year, either by assistance in difficulties such as malpresentation, or purely, in many instances, by the removal of membranes and mucus to enable the calf to breath normally.

IMPORTANCE OF COLOSTRUM

The importance of colostrum to the calf cannot be overstressed. As well as being highly nutritious and easily absorbed by the digestive system, colostrum also supplies the calf with sufficient antibodies, to tide it over the vital early part of its life when it is obviously exposed to infection. Far too often a calf is never allowed a chance to suckle its dam. I appreciate of course that a heifer in particular, who has never seen its calf, does not fret for it.

A good strong calf, and not necessarily the biggest who may be a bit 'dozy' for a while, will soon suckle and obtain its necessary feed and antibodies. Recent surveys have shown, however, that leaving a calf with its dam for 24 hours is no guarantee that it will have suckled. These surveys have been carried out in particular with calf groups, by blood analysis, ascertaining whether a calf has had sufficient colostrum. Even in the hurly burly of looking after large herds, where time is at a premium, a little time, care and attention may reap an enormous amount of benefit in calf rearing, directly in saving calves' lives, making calf-rearing easier and obviating the need for veterinary treatment.

It is often difficult, particularly with the larger herd, to give a calf its own mother's milk for the first 72 hours of its life, but it is well worth while if milk from the newly-calved cow can be fed to its offspring before the milk gets cold. The value of important antibodies decreases rapidly as milk cools. If possible, newly-calved cows should be milked last in a parlour, to prevent contamination of the plant with colostrum, and also there is more time then to get this new milk to the calf.

Ideally, a cow or heifer calves unassisted in a field on her own. This is probably as clean an area as we could wish for, but of course this is not always possible, particularly for winter- or early-spring-calving cows, or animals who have got into difficulty.

At the Welsh Agricultural College, all the cows are housed in cubicles, and we calve them all from January to March. It is extremely dangerous to calve in the cubicle shed, firstly because the cow may get entangled in a cubicle, and secondly, because the new-born calf that is born into a thoroughfare may be trodden on. Every effort, therefore, must be made to remove the cow before calving. Unfortunately, no farm has an inexhaustible supply of boxes, but a good alternative is a straw yard which holds eight to ten cows.

THE NEW-BORN CALF

On calving, the cow and calf are removed to an individual box, or before if assistance is needed. It is essential to move the newly-calved cow and calf soon, otherwise another motherly cow will often adopt the calf and allow it to suckle, thereby depriving her own calf, which may not be born for a few days, of the first draw of essential colostrum. A few minutes spent with a calf and its dam soon after birth will often pay dividends, making sure the calf suckles and obtains its essential and often vital colostrum. Let us hope that these few minutes spent with a new-born calf may be rewarding physically as well as financially, and that calf values of the future are commensurate with the importance of the calf.

One disadvantage of leaving the calf with its mother, apart from making the dam restless as mentioned earlier, is that the calf now has to be re-trained to drink from a bucket unless of course it is to be reared by a suckler cow or mechanical feeder. This can be a problem requiring patience and skill, a point often forgotten with disastrous results when an unskilled person is put to feed calves who may not have the patience for this important job.

It is also as well to remember that drinking from a bucket at floor level is completely unnatural for the young calf, holding the bucket up will help this, and will also help in the calf's well-being. The calf in its early life has a mechanical device, the oesophageal groove, which ensures that the calf's milk by-passes the first three stomachs (the undeveloped rumen, reticulum and omasum) into the fourth stomach (the abomasum) where it curdles and becomes more digestible. When the calf's head is down whilst drinking from a bucket, this oesophogeal groove cannot close properly to form a 'by-pass' pipe, and milk 'spills' into the rumen. This can cause upsets of the digestive tract and scouring.

Like human babies, the calf needs a warm, dry, clean bed, free from draughts particularly, and a fairly high constant temperature with humidity not too high. A warm environment is essential, as like all young animals, the calf's heat control system takes time to 'tune in'. A dry bed is essential for comfort, and of course cleanliness is essential to prevent the pick up of disease from previous occupants of the rearing area. Treatment of the navel at birth with a bacteriostat may help in preventing the introduction to the body of disease bacteria, particularly navel or joint ill.

REARING METHODS

There are enormous variations in the methods of rearing calves, from purpose-built controlled environment calf-houses, to temporary straw-bale houses, which are burnt after each batch of calves, and of course all combinations in between. In my opinion there is no replacement for straw as a comfortable clean lie for calves, but calves are, on the other hand, successfully and economically reared on slats. Bucket feeding is probably the most widely used method of feeding, but self-feeders and automatic electronic batch feeders can work well provided care is taken and that in each and every case a good stockman is responsible for the system.

A novel system of housing calves has been developed at Frondeg Farm. These have been christened 'calf cubes' by our students. The necessity arose at Frondeg to have a fairly large number of calf rearing pens available at once for a batch spring-calving herd.

1. A clean, controlled environment, draught-proof calf house with individual feeding arrangements.

2. A simple method of adapting wooden cow cubicles to a roomy calf house for rearing autumn-born calves at the Welsh Agricultural College.

Buildings previously used for calf-rearing were stone-walled, cold and damp, creating conditions of high humidity, in which calves frequently developed pneumonia.

We wanted an effective solution to our calf-rearing, without incurring the fairly high expense of building a calf-rearing house, for which we neither had the money nor the time to build. Fortunately, we had a Dutch barn with a high roof, which formed an overall umbrella. Below this the rearing pens were built in groups of four, the basis of each group of four pens being second quality plywood measuring $8' \times 4' \times \frac{3}{4}''$ (2·5 m × 1·22 m × 19 mm). Doors were cut out and two bucket holders fixed, one for water and one for an early-wean mix, but used also to hold the milk bucket at feeding. When in position 3' (914 mm) wide chicken wire is laid on top, which supports an insulating layer of well shaken straw.

I have described this system in detail as it has been extremely successful and satisfies to a very large extent the ideal conditions necessary for successful calf-rearing. The pen is warm, as the calf generates its own heat, much of which is maintained in the pen by the insulating layer of straw. The gap in front of the pen, however, allows foul air to be dispelled freely and this prevents the build-up of humid conditions. It is very noticeable on a cold winter's day how warm it is in these boxes, compared with the air outside.

These boxes are fully draught-proof as there is no way for draughts to enter. There is no base, and clean straw forms the bedding area. The boxes are easily cleaned; being without a floor, they can be picked up with a foreloader leaving the muck behind, and are left out in the rain to soak, pressure washed or scrubbed and, when dry, creosoted. This means that one is effectively using new premises every time they are used, and every calf rearer knows how much an advantage it is to rear calves in new premises.

Bucket holders ensure a supply of water and concentrates, and a horse hay net, hung from a nail at the top of each pen, allows the calf access from an early age to a clean, easily available supply of hay.

Incidence of disease has been minimal with this system, cross contamination between calves is non-existent, and it allows control of vices such as navel or udder sucking. The construction of the pens means that calves have to be humped in, a fairly easy job at two days old. It is a little more difficult to remove the calves, but two persons, one inside and one outside, can manage this surprisingly easily when the animals are six weeks of age, usually about a week after weaning.

The cost of these pens was £3·50 in 1971 and £7·00 each in 1972. With the increase in price of wood, the cost in 1975 was around £11 per calf, which is still a relatively cheap, effective calf pen when compared with a purpose-built system. A cheap roof is all that is required, but the building must not be too enclosed as pneumonia may be induced. We have in fact reared up to four successive calves in one pen without cleaning, merely by adding more straw between calves. During the winter of 1974 we very successfully reared calves in these boxes in the open, with only a very cheap tin roof covering the calves.

This is an effective system, but there are obviously many other equally good and successful systems in use. Wooden, free-standing pens in a building, such as those used at the National Agricultural Centre at Stoneleigh work very well, and depend on either forced input or extraction of air, with a straw base. A pen of 2' 6" × 4' (·762 m × 1·22 m) is adequate until six weeks, and this system is easily dismantled. Pens of about the same size are used for purpose-built specialised calf-houses, and temperature sensors control the inflow or outflow of air, making sure that calves are not subject to draughts, or that there is no build-up of stale air pockets in the building.

Many farms have steel partitioning and of course it is recognised that these are more easily cleaned and disinfected. At Bowood I developed a highly successful calf-rearing unit, with calves in pens of four. Cross suckling was a problem but easily overcome by yoking the calves, which ensured that they remained unable to suckle their pen mates until their noses were dry. This unit was able to house up to a hundred calves at a time in old converted, but fairly airy buildings. Losses were very low indeed thanks to excellent stockmanship on the part of George French, who could rear calves as well, if not better, than anyone I have ever met.

OUTDOOR CALF REARING

A system of outdoor calf-rearing in spring and summer has much to commend it. At the Grassland Research institute at Hurley in particular this system has been used with calves suckling from a commercial cold milk churn. Results have been good, although calves drink a phenomenal amount of milk about 56 lb (25·4 kg) compared with a bucket fed calf's average of 28 lb (12·7 kg).

Autumn-calving herds can often enjoy the benefits of rearing calves in individual pens by converting the cubicles, particularly in July, August and September into calf boxes. Many farmers have built special fronts with bucket holders, which are very effective.

At Frondeg, although we have no heifer calves to rear at this time of year, we have, however, to rear some 80–100 bull calves destined for the beef and sheep unit at our Tanygraig Farm. Photograph 2 shows this system. We simply staple pig netting across the fronts of the wooden cow cubicles and straw the cubicle floors. On removal of the calf this straw-muck layer gives a good foundation for the cow's bed in winter.

Much progress has been made in recent years in calf-feeding prior to weaning. The introduction of high fat milk has been very successful for energy intake, but perhaps the most revolutionary, and also on the face of it, an unusual husbandry technique, is the use of cold milk, especially when fed once a day.

This system is now so well established that I need only mention its advantages. It is simple, effective, and its reduction in labour demand make it an attractive proposition, particularly as calves can be fed in the 'off-peak' period of the herdsman's day, say once a day at 10.30 am and not the traditional times, at the same time or directly after each milking.

Numerous experiments have proved that this system is effective, and equally good results are obtained when compared with twice-a-day warm milk feeding.

One feature I have noticed is that calves, after feeding, are far more placid and do not bawl when disturbed. They also take concentrates much sooner, and nibble hay at two–three days old, which again makes for earlier and easier weaning.

When discussing calf-rearing systems, it is dangerous to discuss quantities of feed used at any one time as concentration change and vary between manufacturers. Constituents also vary, with the substitution of animal and vegetable fats, and even the use of warm fresh milk in many farms. I can only say that one has to refer closely to the directions for any milk substitute that is being used.

USE OF CONCENTRATES

The use of concentrates is another matter. The earlier they are used the better, to ensure that the calf at weaning age is eating a sufficient quantity. A good palatable mix with a high digestibility, is essential. In the initial stages, the calf's rumen is not developed, but this is where the use of good clean hay, to help develop this organ, is vital. I am not sure if the traditional soft hay is the best for calves, as it has been shown that coarser hay—but not too coarse—which is sweet to smell may be more beneficial in speeding up the development of the rumen, enabling a quicker change over from the expensive milk diet, to the relatively less expensive concentrate diet.

To achieve palatability one can rely on feed manufacturers' calf pellets, which are formulated for the purpose, or one can also purchase or mix one's own coarse calf ration. Ingredients such as flaked maize, molassine meal and oats improve palatability to entice the calf to feed at an early age.

Weaning a calf has always been a controversial matter. I have always used the 'abrupt' method, where the calf becomes hungry, and helps itself to dry feed. With a Friesian calf, weaning is dependent on his eating some 2 lb (0·90 kg) per day of concentrates, usually around five weeks of age. The trouble with gradual weaning, that is, cutting down the quantity of milk daily, is that the calf still expects its milk and often waits for it, but does not compensate for lack of milk by eating concentrates, and may be underfed for this particular period of stress, and is therefore vulnerable to diseases.

I have only briefly mentioned the diseases to which the calf is subject. These are unfortunately many and are more suitable for a veterinary book. Many can be effectively controlled by good husbandry, the most important being the 'virus pneumonia' complex. The symptoms of breathlessness, high temperature, and heaving are often seen, the worst month being probably November on damp, warmish days when a lot of calves are being fed together.

Good ventilation is the best remedy, by the use of Yorkshire or spaced boarding or open-fronted buildings. A calf after weaning can stand up to far more than we give it credit, provided it is dry. Open-fronted sheds are invaluable for this purpose and many a calf has died through the farmer or herdsman being 'too kind' to it by closing doors and windows. If, however, the calf is wet and in a draught, this is lethal as a wet calf quickly loses body heat and is subject to chills and pneumonia.

SPOTTING THE AILING CALF

A good stockman can very easily spot the ailing calf. Effective treatment is fairly easily carried out using antibiotics, but always under veterinary supervision. Joint ill or navel ill take a big toll of calves and can be controlled by navel dressing and clean quarters, but there is no doubt that it is scouring and consequent dehydration that accounts for the vast majority of calf deaths. Scouring may vary from nutritional scouring through too much milk, to more dangerous and lethal types, such as those caused by *Salmonella* bacteria. These types are often extremely difficult to distinguish, other than by veterinarians and the use of investigational laboratories. This is a highly specialised topic. I can only remind calf rearers that cleanliness and the control of humidity can go a long way towards the prevention of these often lethal and expensive diseases.

Until now we have discussed the calf up to weaning. The feeding of the heifer calf from weaning to some three months of age is probably the most standard of all. From about 10 to 12 weeks, the palatable ration described earlier can be reduced and replaced by rolled barley or oats, or a mixture of both, coupled with either a protein/mineral supplement, or a proprietary concentrate cube or pellet may be used. I have always allowed calves to feed *ad lib* until they are eating 4 lb (1·8 kg) per day and then restricted intake at this level. Good hay is essential to around three months, although some farmers introduce silage much earlier. I have always thought that calves always seem to be 'bloomier' after switching, gradually of course, from hay, however good, to good silage. When we remember such a wet summer as 1974 we realise the advantages of having to make the minimum of hay.

Spring- or summer-born calves at three months are better outside on good 'clean' grass, either grass that has not been grazed by adult stock or calves the previous year, or alternatively on a new ley. This is to eliminate as far as possible the source of infective worm larvae for the young calf.

Very often in practice there is not this 'right' type of grass available in late April; it is too early for new seeds, and other grass will have got away, and one often has to wait until after first-cut silage is taken or even after hay-making.

It is better to turn calves out to a bare pasture immediately after cutting. Hay and concentrates are offered just as they were inside, and this allows the grass to grow 'towards' the calf, and minimises digestive troubles.

Autumn-born calves may of course be turned out very much earlier in late March or early April. Again it is advisable to turn onto a bare 'clean' field, and some sort of shelter is essential, either a run-back to a shed or a good hedge. This is where the advantages of airy winter quarters pay off, as the calf is far more hardy than if it had been in a very enclosed area over winter.

Chapter 4

DAIRY YOUNG STOCK

THE CALF, UP to some three to four months old, has been discussed in Chapter 3. It is a purely arbitrary decision as to when a calf should progress to the category 'dairy young stock'.

It is as well to have objectives in mind prior to discussing methods of achieving them. It is now recognised that it is very desirable for a Friesian heifer at calving to be in the region of 1,100–1,150 lb (498–521 kg) liveweight, or 1,000–1,050 lb (453–476 kg) liveweight immediately after the birth of her calf. Similarly, an Ayrshire heifer will be around 950 lb (430 kg) after calving and a Jersey 800 lb (363 kg).

In considering these aims, we must remember that there are many different methods of rearing, season of calving and age of calving. These range from calving heifers all the year round, to calving on a strictly seasonal pattern, normally in spring or autumn. Age of first calving varies from under two years to over three, but rarely, with reasonable management, over this age.

Bearing in mind all these variables, it is difficult to envisage how one can begin to discuss methods of rearing and feeding used to achieve a satisfactory calving heifer. Success depends on one's ability to produce a heifer that will perform as near to the standards required by that herd as possible. It is no good expecting a heifer calving at less than two years of age, in lean condition, to give 1,200 gallons (5,455 litres). Similarly, in a heavily-fed herd, a heifer calving at two years six months and giving 650 gallons (2,954 litres) will not be received with joy.

AGE OF CALVING

Probably the ideal age of calving a Friesian heifer is two years three months to two years eight months. A Jersey, on the other hand, is very much more early-maturing and can calve very easily and satisfactorily at two years of age. To maintain a set calving pattern in any herd, heifers must either calve at two years or three years of age, and not somewhere in between, as I have indicated. At Bowood this was achieved simply by calving half the herd in spring, and half in autumn. The advantages gained in spreading the herdsmen's work load is obvious, but what this ensured was that heifers born in spring could calve in the July/September period two and a half years later; similarly, of course, with autumn-born calves calving in spring, thus maintaining a herd balance of spring and autumn calves.

This is the ideal solution. Heifers in each calving period can be calved a month earlier than the cows and thereby have some 13 months' period before calving their second. This allows them to grow and develop as well as milk in their first lactation, as they are not put in calf for four months after calving. It also ensures that there is no 'second lactation drop', which is often the case with a heifer calving her second calf within a year of the first.

But what of the herd with a strict spring-calving or autumn-calving pattern? Their choice is either calving at two years or three years, in each case an expensive operation. Calving at two years, to achieve heifer size, means keeping the heifer going at a fair pace from birth to calving. Calving at three years involves keeping the heifer for a long time on the farm and tying up a lot of money over that period.

Although the feed used may be cheaper, more land is used which could be used for higher return enterprises, particularly to keep more cows, and this has to be charged against heifer rearing.

A recent Ministry of Agriculture survey has shown also that calving at three years can give more calving problems than at two and a half years. The results showed that calving problems were reduced as one approached two and a half years, compared with younger calving, and again increased from two and a half to three years.

CALVING HEIFERS AT TWO YEARS IN SPRING

At Frondeg we maintain a strictly spring-calving herd. Cows calve in the January-March period, and all Friesian heifer calves are born by mid-February, as we only use Friesian inseminations for six weeks followed by a Hereford bull that 'mops up' any remaining cows not in calf.

Calves are put out to grass as soon as first-cut silage is removed in mid-May, and are treated with 'Dictol'* before turnout on to a bare field, as described in Chapter 3. They are fed 2–3 lb (0·9–1·4 kg) of a coarse calf ration per day followed later by barley feeding throughout their first summer. In mid-July they are wormed. They are housed in mid-October, again wormed, and are fed *ad lib* silage and a barley/protein mix of between 3 and 6 lb (1·4 and 2·8 kg) per day depending on the quality of the silage. With reasonable silage this rarely exceeds 4 lb (1·8 kg) per day. They are turned out to grass in early April in

* Trade name: Allen & Hanburys, London.

3. Spring-born calves must have good clean grazing through their first summer.

4. In-calf heifers must always obtain adequate feeding to achieve target weights, particularly if they are to calve at two years of age.

their second year, at a weight of some 700 lb (317 kg). On April 26th the bull is introduced to them, and happily up to now 30–35 heifers have all been served in some three to four weeks.

Good grass is offered to these calves right through the summer, and a system of set stocking with four calves per acre (10 calves per hectare) works very well. In the summer of 1974, 33 calves on 8 acres (3·2 hectares) of grass gained 1·69 lb (0·76 kg) per day, as is seen from fig 1, and the grass never grew away from them. Nitrogen was applied when there was a tendency for the calves to be getting on top of the sward. At no time, however, was there an abundance of grass.

THE SECOND SUMMER

In their second summer good grass is again offered. Thirty-four heifers in 1974 were maintained from April 6th to September 15th on 14 acres (5·7 hectares) of grass, and 6 acres (2·4 hectares) of this area was cut for silage twice, and they gained at a rate of 1·64 lb (0·73 kg) per day. A grazing system involving four blocks was used and this allowed some areas to be cut for silage. These cattle were wormed in mid-July and again on housing in mid-October, and fed *ad lib* silage and 3–4 lb (1·4–1·8 kg) barley/protein mix. This ration was gradually increased five weeks before calving in February to 8 lb (3·6 kg) per day.

Using this method, we have repeatedly been able to achieve a heifer of at least 1,000 lb (450 kg) after calving, which we regard as satisfactory and necessary to maintain our calving pattern in January-February. A summary of the performance of a typical batch of two-year-old spring-calving heifers which calved in February 1975 is given in figs 1 and 2—with physical results in fig 1 and financial results in fig 2 on pages 39 and 40.

It may surprise many dairy farmers who have bought and sold heifers in a mart how these costs add up. When this book is read, no doubt many of the 1974/75 prices, or the projected 1976 prices, will not be applicable, but up-to-date figures can be easily superimposed. If interest is charged on the money that is tied up throughout the rearing period of these heifers, as it should, this will again increase the final real cost to over £200. At the time of writing, good heifers were easily obtained at prices well below this figure. This poses the eternal question: Should we rear our replacements?

Every heifer entering the herd also has at least another, a year younger, on the farm. This 'pair' is often referred to as a 'replacement unit', which in terms of feed requirements, particularly grassland requirement, is equivalent to a cow. Scrapping rearing in favour of buying calving heifers would mean that a 100-cow herd, requiring

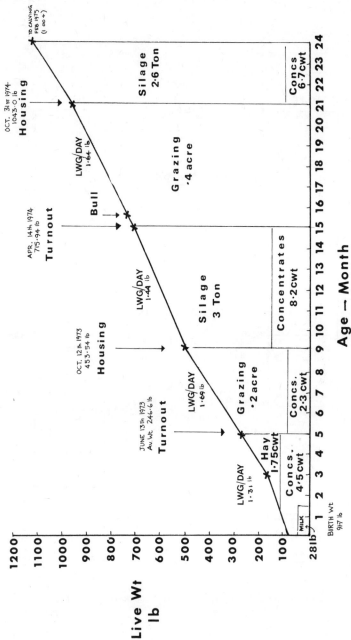

Fig. 1. Liveweight gain feeding of spring-born dairy heifer calving at two years—physical results.

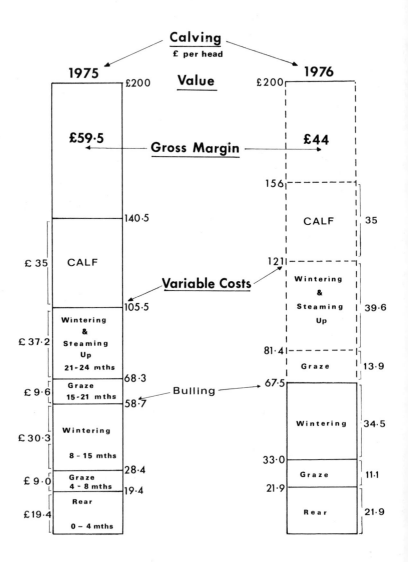

Fig. 2. Two-year-old dairy heifers—a two-year comparison of financial results.

some 25 heifers a year, could be increased to 125 cows. Many of the costs of maintaining these extra cows are marginal; machinery costs would not be greatly increased from that of 100 cows, buildings could often be adapted to house an extra 25 cows, particularly as heifer sheds are released, a parlour for 100 could almost certainly be stretched to milk the extra cows. In fact, on the face of it, it looks a worthwhile switch, why therefore do not many more farmers do this?

It would indeed be disastrous and self-destructive if too many farmers relied on buying heifer replacements. There would be an inadequate supply of heifers, and of course the demand for these and their cost would rise dramatically, and we would return to a situation where it would be cheaper to rear our own. Another example of the swings and roundabouts of competitive farming! But in any event, whatever the overall policy, heifer calves from the best cows should always be reared.

Land away from the farm, inaccessible to milking cows, can often support heifer rearing. There is of course the pride and satisfaction of rearing one's own heifers, choosing bulls, and saying to oneself, 'My next lot of heifers are going to be toppers'. This itself goes a long way to maintain an active interest and enthusiasm towards farming, without which it could become a sad and unhappy industry, particularly when a herd has to be milked 14 times a week, 52 weeks a year.

There is in many of us, the desire to become a master breeder, even if only on a small scale. Constant battling to improve one's herd, goes a very long way towards trying to achieve this aim.

WHAT BREED OF BULL?

The selection of a bull to use on heifers is always a point that generates discussion. With increased calf values, the widespread use of an Aberdeen Angus bull, purely for ease of calving, has lost favour. The Hereford running with a group of heifers is used extensively, particularly in view of its docility, its availability and the reasonable ease of calving of its progeny. It is always useful to use a young Hereford bull on a few mature cows in the first year, to establish whether or not his calves are easily born.

The use of the 'red breeds', the Lincoln Red, the Sussex and, particularly recently, the more popular Red Ruby of North Devon origin has gained favour. The advantages are that a good calf, of higher value than the Angus cross is produced. We have found at the College also that the Devon-cross Friesian heifer also makes an excellent suckler cow, docile, not too big, and with plenty of milk.

Many dairy heifers, particularly the Friesian, are bred pure.

Running young dairy bulls with heifers is relatively easy as they are fairly quiet up to the age of 18 to 20 months, and an overfat young bull can be improved considerably by losing flesh and getting plenty of exercise with a group of heifers. The case for breeding heifers pure may be important with a young or expanding herd requiring the maximum number of heifer calves, but in many instances it is advisable to rear replacements off proven females only.

Up to now I have only discussed running the heifers with a bull, as this is probably how 90 per cent of our heifers are put in calf. One can of course inseminate, the problem being knowing exactly which heifers are bulling when they are in a mob, and the daily chore of handling and yarding them, as distinct from cows which have to be yarded anyway for milking.

HOW MANY HEIFERS PER BULL?

How many heifers to a bull is also an eternal question. A mature Hereford or Friesian will handle 30 to 40 in a group quite well provided he is fit, not too fat, and particularly if his feet are sound. The actual number depends to a large extent on the bull's temperament. One Hereford bull at Frondeg, now over five years of age, *Little Tarrington Junior*, has never been seen to serve a heifer yet, but 25 calves by him were born in four weeks in 1974. He obviously does not waste energy, as do some bulls, repeatedly serving a heifer. He also has an odd habit, which may be related, of sitting on his backside, like a dog, surveying his harem. He may be of the same family as the two bulls in the well known story!

The largest group of heifers I have ever introduced to bulls is 130, in Bowood. Three newly bought strong 18-month-old Herefords were turned in with the heifers and, contrary to expectation, no fighting took place at all as they were far too busy, as was evident from the furious rate of calving nine months later.

One of the biggest reasons for loss of heifers is difficulty at calving, possibly on a par in importance with the deadly ravaging and infuriating summer mastitis. It is a heartbreaking sight, to see a potentially good heifer, having had a difficult calving, lose flesh rapidly, and often even be unable to get up for several days after calving. It is imperative, therefore, to have a calf born that is not too big. I have already mentioned how this can be achieved by the use of bulls, either of a small breed, or bulls who are known to produce smaller calves. The use of the new Continental breeds on heifers is certainly not to be recommended, except perhaps the Chianina with its long narrow body, but there is insufficient evidence yet about the use of this breed.

'STEAMING UP' HEIFERS

Feeding of the heifer is all-important towards this end. The calf grows rapidly over the last few weeks of pregnancy, and overfeeding heifers at this time can cause trouble. This can be overcome in winter fairly easily. A 'fit' heifer can be kept at an even plane of nutrition for the last three or four weeks, and should not be 'steamed up' to excess. In summer, the provision of good grass can cause the same difficulties, and often after a good summer, autumn calving heifers can produce big calves. It is as well to remember, provided ample good grass is available, no concentrates are required for steaming up, and not only in relation to difficult calving. A heifer that has 'bagged up' too much will mean that later, as a cow, she will 'lose' her bag far sooner than a heifer calved down without an over-developed udder.

One point that has always impressed me is that a heifer, calved by Caesarean section, recovers far quicker and milks better than a heifer which has suffered badly from a bad calving. I fully appreciate that there is a very definite limit to the number of such operations that can be performed in terms of a vet's time, and of course they are not cheap, but are often cheaper in terms of a live calf and increased milk production during the lactation due to less damage to the heifers at calving.

WHERE TO CALVE

Probably the best place to calve heifers is in a field, near the steading, where one can keep an eye on them. Heifers take longer to calve than a cow, and much damage can be done by interfering, as a heifer takes time to relax her pelvis. When to give assistance to a heifer can only be judged by the stockman's experience.

Winter calving of course is best done in a good deep-strawed box or yard, but never on concrete as the heifer, in particular, is subject to splaying of her hind legs on slippery surfaces. Leg muscles and often the nerves of the hind quarters and legs can be slightly to severely damaged at calving. At any sign of splaying, when a heifer is walking 'wide', it is advisable to tie the hind legs together, just above the hocks, using a thick large diameter rope, allowing some 12 to 14 inches (304–355 mm) of movement between the legs. Heifers and cows can walk quite easily with this attachment, and this allows the tissues to recover, rather than be further, and often irreparably, damaged by the animal doing the 'splits'.

Chapter 5

THE GRAZING HERD

WHEN WE LOOK at milk production results we see that, in many instances, for every gallon (4·54 litres) of milk produced throughout the year, 3 or even 4 lb (1·36–1·81 kg) of concentrates have been fed. MMB LCP results of all recorded farms in 1975 showed that for every gallon of milk produced 3·5 lb (1·6 kg) of concentrates were fed in the 1,956 recorded herds. We are quite used to herds achieving 1,000 gallons (4,546 litres) sold and using in excess of 20 cwt (1,016 kg) of concentrates; this means 3·5 lb (1·6 kg) concentrates fed for every gallon (4·54 litres) produced.

We all know that grass can be made to produce milk, but from these results it makes one doubt whether the vast majority of farmers realise this and still regard the grass and grass products part of the cow's ration as little more than for her maintenance.

ARE WE USING OUR GRASS EFFICIENTLY?

It was a sad reflection on our grassland management in Britain when Mac McKenzie, a senior New Zealand Dairy Board adviser commented in an article in the Milk Marketing Board publication, *Better Management*, in January 1975, that of the 200 farms he visited in the summer of 1974 in Britain, only six could pass as efficient grassland managers (I can only hope that we were one of the six). He quotes from what must have been a New Zealand inspired poem:

> *'Many a grass is born to blush unseen*
> *And waste its nutrients in the British scene!'*

I am assured that he is not referring to long grass at Cardiff Arms Park designed to trip up the 'All Blacks'!

The figures quoted above are admittedly average figures, and many farmers are able to show a far more economical use of both grass and concentrates. The payment structure for milk has, however, encouraged this type of production and has made the use of concentrates profitable, provided it is matched with good cowmanship. It is also almost certainly true that, in the near future, cereal- and protein-based concentrates will be less available, more expensive, and will be required by a hungry world to feed humans directly rather than be fed in the relatively inefficient process to animals, to be processed into milk and particularly into beef.

There is no doubt that it is easier to rely on concentrates to produce milk both in summer and winter; shortages of grazing or fodder in winter can be corrected and compensated for at all times merely by adding a few extra pulls to the feed hopper in the milking parlour. Indeed I cannot blame farmers who have adopted and maintained this policy, as the milk price structure has encouraged this, but as mentioned earlier, there is no doubt that resorting to this method will become less profitable, or even impossible.

USE OF NITROGEN

I will now discuss methods of grazing in current use where economic milk production depends on the use of grass at a relatively high stocking rate, which invariably means a considerable input of fertiliser nitrogen. In the depths of pessimism, I can also pursue the same argument as I used for the use of concentrates. Nitrogenous fertiliser production is based on fossil fuels, and its availability has to be considered. Will price, availability, and environmental considerations governing the use of this raw material, force us to use less, and adopt lower stocking rates than the ones with which we are accustomed?

AIMS AT FRONDEG

In the last few years, under the conditions and prices prevailing, my aims have been fairly simple. Under West Wales conditions of normally adequate rainfall (more than adequate in many instances) I have aimed to achieve a stocking rate of a cow to the acre (2·2 cows per hectare), 250–280 units of nitrogen per acre (600–670 units per hectare) and 1,000 gallons (4,546 litres) sold per cow, using 14–15 cwt (711–762 kg) of concentrates. In 1974, this gave a margin over concentrates of £200+. At Aberystwyth we have achieved this with a spring-calving herd, and of course our sights are now set higher, particularly as the herd improves. Another 100 gallons (454 litres) sold per cow should be possible without raising our inputs other than management and herdsmanship, making better silage, growing better grass and culling some of our lower yielders as the herd develops.

TRUE STOCKING RATES

A discussion on stocking rates is always very interesting as, in my opinion, it is of no use whatsoever comparing figures if one does not refer to concentrate use at the same time. To quote a ridiculous example, an acre of concrete can support probably 1,000 cows, feeding all the year round on barley straw and concentrates, and stocking rate and milk *per acre* here can be enormous. In the same way, when a cow is fed two tons or more concentrates per annum, it is difficult to justify why she has to have another one and a half acres (0·6 hectares) of grass to support her. When calculating stocking rates, we should take into account the concentrate use as well. A milk producer may be proud of his stocking rate of one cow per acre, but his 1,100 gallon (4,994 litres) herd may be using 33 cwt (1,676 kg) of barley also. This, in my mind, adds up to another acre (0·4 hectare) used, consequently his true stocking rate is one cow per two acres (0·8 hectares), and his 1,100 gallons per acre (12,330 litres per hectare) quickly becomes half of this figure, which is now nowhere near the league leaders.

This was brought to my attention in New Zealand, where there is no correction factor for concentrate usage in most herds. The best of the dairy farmers there are producing 500+ Jb of butterfat per acre (560 kg of butterfat per hectare). This is the equivalent of 1,250 gallons per acre (14,032 litres per hectare) of milk sold at 4 per cent butterfat without the use of any concentrates at all. This was a figure that really made one think and gave me a completely new set of aims.

GRAZING SYSTEMS

We are faced with an enormous problem when discussing grazing systems, as these vary from area to area with climatic differences, the topography of the farm, type of farming, size of farm and possibly most important the personal choice of the man involved. One other important aspect of choice of grazing system is what I call 'the bandwagon effect', a new system being devised and its use becoming widespread very quickly.

In County Cork, 720 gallons milk sold per acre (8,110 litres per hectare) with 2–3 cwt (101–152 kg) of concentrates per cow per annum, is regarded as a peak of achievement. In south-east England of course, where grass growth slows down and may even stop in midsummer, with pastures often continuing bare until late autumn, other feeding regimes, often from cereal-based concentrates, have to be resorted to, and also of course the other feeds—brewers' grains, sugarbeet tops, zero-grazed maize or lucerne—have to be made available. The rest of the country falls somewhere, to varying degrees, between these two extremes.

Much of the credit for grazing management progress is due to the fertiliser companies. No doubt their preachings sold a considerable amount of fertiliser, and in fairness, this is their job, but there is no

5. Adequate grass allows a herd to lie down and produce milk (Frondeg, June 1975).

6. Early spring grass is valuable and must be rationed carefully.

doubt whatsoever that these companies have 'awakened' many farmers to realise grassland potential and have been responsible for a very large number of farmers being involved in highly efficient and profitable systems on their farms.

THE SIMPLE ELECTRIC FENCE

It is now taken so much for granted, that one may forget that the man who first electrified a cheap single strand of wire to control his cows has been responsible for enormous developments and improvements in managing and utilising our grassland with the dairy cow. We can now argue that possibly there is no need for subdivision, but it was the building-up period to this current widespread doctrine, with subdivision, either as strip-grazing or formal paddocks, which allowed a system to be planned and the operator to gain confidence by forward budgeting of feed supplies, both for grazing and conservation. This normally reduces the danger of shortage, which is critical, thus allowing an increase in stocking rate followed by an increase in production, and very often profitability.

THE PADDOCK SYSTEM

For years the questions that have been asked whenever paddock grazing systems were discussed are: "How many, what size, whether 24- or 12-hour, whether long and narrow or square, and how many water points?" As a base I will discuss our system at Frondeg, where we have 102 cows.

We have worked with 24 paddocks for the last four years, each of 2·2 acres (0·89 hectare) which gives a total paddock area of 53 acres (21·5 hectares) or half an acre (0·2 hectares) per cow, and a grazing intensity (that is, the number of cows per acre or per hectare at any one time) of 50 cows per acre (124 cows per hectare) which may be regarded by some as a little high.

WHEN TO TURN OUT IN SPRING

Cows are turned out to an area of RvP Italian ryegrass as soon as conditions and grass growth permits in spring, usually around March 20th. They are also allowed grazing areas destined for conservation, and it is only when we know that sufficient grass in one paddock for 24 hours' grazing will be available towards the end of the cycle that we begin grazing the paddocks.

In most years the first 10 to 12 paddocks supply only 12 hours' grazing in the first cycle. By the time that we are half way through this cycle, that is, after about a week (which is a very long time, especially in a slow growing late spring). Sufficient grass is then usually available on the ungrazed paddocks to hold the cows for 24 hours. Indeed grass growth is normally so rapid at that time, that we are able to 'by-pass' three or even four paddocks, leaving them to be cut for silage. It is important to organise the system so that these paddocks are easily cut, and not be left with paddocks too steep to approach with a forage harvester. It is also important to cut these paddocks first for silage, so that regrowth can be made available for grazing as soon as possible. This is usually in mid-May, which means that the grass is removed before there is too much basal shading and consequent yellowing and a slow recovery of the sward.

Normally, cows now rotate around the paddock system. The first application of 40–50 units of nitrogen in late February, or as soon as the land is dry and firm enough to carry a tractor, is followed by the application of 30–40 units of nitrogen after each grazing. Up to recently, phosphate reserves were maintained by triennial application of 10 cwt per acre (1,255 kg per hectare) of 12–14 per cent P_2O_5 basic slag and mid-summer application of a compound fertiliser, cumulating in 1974 with 270 units of nitrogen, 60 units of phosphate and 60 units of potash over the whole of the grazing area.

USE OF POTASH

The application of potash is very interesting. We have been told, and indeed soil analyses have indicated, that under an intensive dairy grazing system there is little need for more than some 40–50 units of potash applied in midsummer with the massive recirculation of dung and urine in this system. Many areas in west Wales are naturally potash deficient and we have had a marked response to the application of potash to our paddocks in midsummer. Potash requirements are far from resolved, and current results on intensive dairy pastures in Cumbria indicate that there may be many other areas of Britain potash-hungry.

The Cumbria Grassland Society led by Mr Edwin Bushby of Egremont, together with the Grassland Research Institute and the Ministry of Agriculture, have begun a series of experiments to establish the potash need and response of their pastures. Preliminary results indicate strongly that with higher potash applications, palatability is improved, cows graze pastures more evenly, and there is far less sod-pulling, which was becoming a major problem on some of these farms. This latter effect is probably due to the combination of the effect of palatability and closer grazing, and the consequent development of a stronger, and particularly, a deeper root system when adequate potash is available. This has resulted also, in particular on Mr Bushby's farm, in a reduction in nitrogen usage, by increased potash usage from 40–50 units to an average of 120 units over the whole farm.

To return to Frondeg, two or three paddocks, not usually the same ones as cut first time round, may again become available for second cut silage, but this is dependent on growth conditions.

SPRING CALVERS ARE HUNGRY

With a spring-calving herd receiving no concentrates after the first few weeks at grass, when it is fed as a magnesium carrier, our paddocks are subject to a more testing time than most. They have to support a mob of very hungry cows in full milk and therefore eating at least 150 per cent of the amount eaten by a cow in late lactation or dry. There is also no 'buffering' effect by using concentrates in lean times, where often a considerable proportion of a cow's requirements has been fed in the parlour, thereby making less demand on the grassland available. We have managed with this system at Frondeg, and one must remember that this is not a farmlet situation but a whole farm test bench, and so there is nowhere else to turn for help in maintaining the herd either in summer or winter.

Any system of commercial milk production, as is ours, must however be flexible. There is no feeling of failure if we have to strip graze outside the paddock area at certain times.

For example, in the dry late spring of 1974 we had to resort to strip grazing part of the area set up for silage, using a paddock for 12 hours' grazing *only,* and supplementing with strip grazing for the other 12 hours. The cows, particularly at this time of year, must have priority as they are at peak yield, and our philosophy always is that silage can be made later if necessary, with the possible use of more fertiliser nitrogen to compensate for time.

MIDSUMMER GRAZING

As the summer progresses, particularly after silage-making in mid-August, more land becomes available, and at this time, a combination of a paddock by day and strip grazing aftermaths by night is used. As cows dry off in October, they are removed from the milkers to the conservation area, and therefore the grazing intensity progressively decreases with the wane in grass growth. This grazing intensity decreases in two ways, firstly, by reduced numbers, and secondly, in that cows at this time drying off have a far lower feed requirement as compared with their demand in spring. In fact what we have tried to do as far as possible, is to match grass growth and consequent availability throughout the grazing year with the needs of the herd.

NUMBER OF PADDOCKS

I appreciate that I have described one 24 paddock system. Some systems in favoured areas can work with 21 or even 18 paddocks, but rarely does the system allow for some cutting with this number. A decrease in the number of paddocks, is very often associated with lower stocking rates of more than half an acre (0·2 hectare) per cow, or with an autumn-calving herd, where demand for feed in summer is less than a cow in full milk.

In some instances sufficient paddocks—up to 40—are made available to allow for 12 hourly changes, and there is no doubt that this system has many advantages in that cows are offered fresh grass at each feed. This is particularly advantageous in times of grass shortage, when cows will settle down after each milking better than if they are returned to a paddock bared by the previous grazing.

Paddock numbers vary from three or four to 40. Three large paddocks are used very successfully, allowing a week on each. A 100-cow herd needs three areas totalling 50–60 acres (20–25 hectares), say, three 20-acre (8 hectare) fields. Similarly, five or six paddocks may be used, possibly six 10-acre (4 hectare) areas, the cows grazing each paddock for three or four days. Whether we regard this as a paddock-grazing system or not is subject to argument, but it works, and this is the most important point.

A paddock-grazing system, as we know it, of around 21 sub-divisions has many direct advantages. One of these is that most farmers who have adopted this system, often because of economic pressures are demanding more output, accompanied by higher stocking rates. As a 'tool' in the adviser's hand, the system is invaluable and simple. Given clear-cut directives, and provided that no attempt is made to overstock or run before one can walk, it is almost guaranteed to give the results predicted, assuming of course that the farmer follows the rules fairly carefully.

In particular, the role of the conservation area can be planned, and under normal conditions feed availability as silage can be fairly accurately predicted within a narrow margin. The prediction of the availability of conserved feed as hay is not so straightforward, as the vagaries of the weather are almost certain to affect timeliness of operations. The whole system then becomes a 'hit or miss' affair, and away goes the main strength of the system, reliability and confidence, with each succeeding rain cloud in the summer months.

The system, particularly as high stocking rates are approached, demands a strict planned system of fertiliser application throughout the grazing season, and as an extra bonus, this allows for careful planning of the buying programme of fertiliser requirements at the right time and at the maximum price advantage. The dairy farmer or herdsman knows that his cows will be in paddock No. 4 on June 1st and again on June 21st, returning again on July 14th. The system, I again stress, has an enormous advantage. It eliminates the difficult decisions that have to be made, such as, 'Do I give five or six yards (4·5 or 5·5 m) when I strip graze?'. I make no apology for repeating that this can also be of help to the adviser who is in the position of wanting to gain the farmer's confidence.

The saving of labour can also be a major advantage of a paddock grazing system. Moving an electric fence twice daily, and moving all the equipment from field to field, even with a mains fencer can take considerable time, seven days a week, and often means, with a large herd, that a second man has to do the job. Too often the fence mover is not as skilled as the man in charge, or sufficiently interested to assess the grass requirement of the herd. A good man can do this very well, by assessing how they have cleared the grass in the last twelve hours, and adjust the forward movement accordingly. Too often, however, the second man, who may be a tractor driver, will not have the information that is available to the milker, who can see signs of under-feeding by a fall in daily milk production. Moving the electric fence forward the correct amount is a highly skilled operation. Changing paddocks means a few seconds, closing one paddock gate and opening another.

I do not want to create the impression that I have 'paddock mania', but as a system it will continue until a better system is discovered and proved. This includes set stocking, which I will discuss later.

WATER SUPPLY

Paddock-grazing systems have disadvantages and the systems employed are by no means a perfect system of grazing. Setting up a paddock system is not cheap, and providing an adequate supply of water is another costly item, particularly on farms with low water pressure, where larger bore $\frac{3}{4}$-inch (19 mm) pipe is required rather than the customary $\frac{1}{2}$-inch (12·7 mm) pipe. Larger troughs may also have to be used to act as reservoirs, filling them particularly during milking time and providing the cows with an ample supply of water immediately after milking, which is a critical time when demand is greatest.

At Frondeg we try and get over this problem of a low pressure water supply in two ways. Firstly, water is freely available in the collecting yard at milking time; secondly, cows also have to pass a large 400-gallon (1820 litre) circular tank on their way from the parlour, and we have fixed 5-foot (1·5 m) diameter, 400-gallon (1820 litre) capacity concrete tanks in the area of the farm where the water pressure is lowest.

Water, although expensive, is still a great deal cheaper than milk. Cows will not walk long distances for their water, even in midsummer, and also they invariably behave as a herd, and therefore all tend to drink in the same periods of the day, thereby creating peak demands which must be satisfied if they are going to drink the amount necessary to produce the maximum potential milk yield.

Ideally, every field or paddock should have a water trough or, more practically, one trough between two. This is not always possible, but I don't like to see cows having to travel more than 500 to 600 yards (450 to 550 m) for their water. This distance is almost certain to reduce daily intake and have a direct and drastic effect on milk yield.

On a hot day it must be remembered that a 6-gallon (27·2 litre) Friesian will drink 40 gallons (180 litres) of water. One hundred cows will produce a hefty demand on a $\frac{1}{2}$-inch (12·7 mm) alkathene pipe, bearing in mind that cows will have access to a trough for only 20 hours per day. There must be a constant rate of flow of 200 gallons (910 litres) per hour at minimum, allowing for constant running during the whole period. If we allow for periods of no demand, such as the mid-morning and night resting periods when all the cows are lying down, we can at least double the rate of flow required to 400 gallons (1,820 litres) per hour to maintain the herd's supply. This means that with a $\frac{1}{2}$-inch (12·7 mm) pipe we need a considerable pressure to maintain this flow. I have dwelt on these points for some time, and they are well worth remembering when setting up a water supply.

DISADVANTAGES OF PADDOCK GRAZING

To return to the disadvantages of paddock grazing, one of these is fouling of pastures by the cows. We could argue, however, that it is no worse than any other system with a comparable stocking rate, other than a fully integrated grazing and cutting system where effective stocking density is halved, and where there is a longer period between actual grazings as cutting is often carried out between them, thus allowing a longer period for degeneration of dung pats.

Set stocking, however, tends to produce a 'camp effect' where cows tend to congregate in very hot or foul weather, usually a different camp for each weather condition. This produces a very large fouling problem in a relatively small area.

In common with many others, I have found that this fouling effect disappears after three or four years continuous use of paddocks for cow grazing. Evidence points to an increase in earthworm populations in these paddocks, and this is particularly evident in spring with the enormous number of earthworm casts that one sees in the base of the sward. This, and the equally dramatic increase in other organisms involved in the breakdown of dung pats, result in their rapid disappearance after this method of grazing has been used for a few years. The problem of refusal of grass by the herd then becomes less acute, and the need for topping either disappears or is required once only in the season.

One major criticism can be levelled at the paddock-grazing system. We have a fixed number of paddocks, each normally providing the herd with sufficient grazing for 24 hours. We know, however, that grass grows more rapidly in May than in July, and there is no inbuilt method of allowing for fluctuating grass availability. With a strip-grazing system, and provided there is expert control, allowances can be made for grass availability.

Edwin Bushby, of Watson Hill, in Cumbria, I would call a master producer of milk from grass. He has relatively small fields for his 122-cow herd, which is a useful factor in that the length of stay in any one field is short, and he still practises strip grazing. He and his sons and his men know how much grass to give his cows daily from years of experience. He really has a flexible paddock system, its size varying with the season and the cows' needs, and he would be very reluctant to change to any other system, but we are not all in the same league as Edwin as grassland managers.

STOCK NEEDS AND GRASS GROWTH

As mentioned earlier, in farm situations with paddocks, relief valves are available, by grazing areas originally meant for conservation in times of stress. When one examines the system carefully, however, there is a marked correlation between stock needs and grass growth. Both autumn- and spring-calving herds need a large quantity of grass in May, when grass growth is at its peak, and also it is good practice not to graze too hard in May, to allow for rapid regrowth. I have always tried, but not always succeeded, not to bare pastures in the early part of the growing season. The leaf remaining 'feeds' the grass plant, thereby increasing grass production. In our case also, it is not our policy to graze a spring-calving herd too hard, as they are in full milk, and grass intake must not be restricted.

Leaf remaining in May produces more leaf and not detrimental seed heads. Later on with the same stocking rate, as growth rate of grass declines, it has the effect of grazing the pasture barer, which is again essential at this time to prevent seed head emergence. Seed heads at any time have two effects, firstly, they denote that the quality of the grass on offer has decreased, and secondly, their presence has the effect of reducing new tiller production in the base of the sward and is therefore directly responsible for slowing down growth. If seed heads appear in profusion, which is sometimes inevitable, topping of the sward as low as possible immediately after grazing is the surest way of retaining a thick rapidly growing sward.

SET STOCKING

Set stocking is the oldest of all grazing systems. Its 're-introduction' has come about, however, with far higher stocking rates than were traditionally employed.

It may seem strange at first, but to me the 'set stocking' or 'range grazing' or 'full graze' system of grazing is merely a follow-on development from the use of paddocks, although both systems seem to be diametrically opposed at first sight. The successful use of paddocks has brought discipline and confidence in the use of fertilisers, higher stocking rates and the planning of conservation requirements, to levels never dreamed of a few years ago. It is these farmers who, in the main, have turned to set stocking.

Of all the set-stocking systems that I have seen, they are all reaping the benefits accrued during the period they have employed paddock grazing systems. Increased stocking rates and controlled grazing have meant rapid improvement in sward quality. An original sward of mixed content, including Yorkshire Fog, bent, crested dogstail and perennial ryegrass, becomes a pure stand of perennial ryegrass with this system of management.

Set stocking relies on the availability and maintenance of a dense, highly tillering sward. Experimental evidence from Northern Ireland, however, shows that the whole sward area is not continuously grazed. Cows, by the very nature of their grazing habits, will only return to an area that has been grazed when it has grown sufficiently for another 'bite' to be available. The average life of a tiller in a perennial ryegrass sward has been recorded as 14 days, and for some six to eight days of its life, it would be below the cows' grazing level. The cow returns to the same area about every week. There is in fact a 'mini rotation' grazing system within the sward in each individual small area of ground cover.

It is extremely detrimental to a set-stocking system to allow grass to 'get away' from the herd in May, and grazing must start before there is much growth in the grazing area. In fact a brand-new discipline has to be learnt in the early part of the year. Normally, no cutting areas can be laid aside within the grazing area, although no system should be as inflexible as not to allow a field within the grazing block to be shut off in times of plenty, or an extra field opened up for grazing when grass is scarce.

These last few comments indicate the main problem of set stocking. If you want to make decisions continuously, then change to a set-stocking system, that is, if you are going to maintain your present stocking rate of half an acre (0·2 hectare) per cow over the grazing area.

ADVANTAGES OF SET STOCKING

We must remember that half an acre (0·2 hectare) of grassland per cow throughout the growing season is a very high stocking rate, and that many set-stocking systems are working at levels well below this. This is particularly true of mainly spring-calving herds. Those I have seen have used between 0·7 and 0·8 acres (0·3 hectare) for grazing, and of course this is a very practical way of meeting the very high grass requirements of these herds.

It is a frightening experience to see a highly stocked farm committed to set stocking in midsummer. There is seemingly very little grass for the cows, but there is no doubt that the cows are content with the system, apparently as they are fully fed and satisfied. Or maybe they have no idea that any other fields exist, and we presume, as they are creatures of habit, that they accept the system.

The only true criterion whether cows are obtaining sufficient feed is to look at the results in the bulk tank, but I must not be cynical as production results per acre on many of these farms are excellent. It may be that two reasons present themselves to explain a certain degree of cynicism. One is that I have been involved for some time in watching, waiting and even praying for grass growth to appear before grazing takes place, and secondly, I cannot put forward a logical, technical explanation why set stocking of cows does work at all, bearing in mind the teachings of the last 70 years.

There are some obvious and direct advantages with set stocking. The provision of water is easier and cheaper, although in a 50-acre (20 hectare) block there is need for three or even four points for water, but these are often already available in many dairying areas in the existing field boundaries. The saving of fencing costs is another advantage, and also of course, particularly on an exposed farm, the cows are able to choose some sheltered areas in foul weather. A hedge, a hollow or even a wall is far more satisfactory shelter in driving rain than the shelter afforded by a single strand of electric wire in the centre paddock of a 20-acre (8 hectare) exposed field.

Fertilising every three or four weeks, or even once per week, reduces the labour requirement substantially, but retains the disciplined planning of regular applications. I have always believed in applying fertiliser nitrogen to paddocks immediately the cows are removed, normally the following morning. In very busy times, I allow two or even three days' grace, and at weekends. My main reasons are as follows: When the nitrogen is on, even in a dry time, the chances of even a light shower or heavy dew washing it in is high, and as soon as it is in the soil it works. With 21–24 paddocks, missing one day when the grass sward is without sufficient nitrogen is critical; one day is 5 per cent of the total cycle, three days is 15 per cent and so on. I have often been asked, 'But why bother—5 per cent is very little'. My answer here is that 5 per cent decrease in production with 100 cows at Frondeg is *five cows less;* with milk at £300+ sold per cow this results in £1,500 less sales per annum, figures which speak for themselves.

Nitrogen or compound fertiliser (but not basic slag) can be applied to the grazing area even when the cows are grazing, seemingly with no harm.

NEW WHITE CLOVERS

With the increased use of nitrogen, we have almost become accustomed to the loss of white clover from our swards. Most of the disappearance is due to the shading effects of the more vigorous growing grasses, particularly in a rotational system where there is an enormous shading effect built up prior to grazing or cutting. The use of a set-stocking system should encourage the come-back of white clover into the sward. This will be a very interesting development to follow in the next few years, although probably some method of introducing white clover, particularly the long-petioled varieties newly available from Aberystwyth (Sabeda and Olwen). Sod seeding, particularly in July, will be a good method of introducing the clovers to the sward.

OTHER GRAZING SYSTEMS

As always, there are many individual varieties of paddock-grazing systems that have received substantial publicity, as they have all worked exceedingly well. I will refer to two systems, namely Mr Stanley Morrey's fully integrated cutting and grazing system, and the Wye College System practised in Kent by Professor William Holmes. If discussing these systems, and comparing them does nothing else, they prove that in agriculture, as in many other fields of work, that it is the man in charge that makes a system work.

Professor Mac Cooper, when at Newcastle Upon Tyne, always referred to such methods as 'Grand Prix' models, comparing them to cars that are pushed to the limit to test new tyres, transmissions and fuels, from which the common motorist benefits ultimately. We always need 'Grand Prix' systems in farming to be emulated, at least in part, by the ordinary farmer.

Mr Stanley Morrey has 42 one-day paddocks, and cows rotate around them. However, as soon as he sees that there is a danger of grass overtaking cows, and the expertise comes in being able to spot this long before it happens, the cows miss four, five, six or even more paddocks and go on to grass that is young, plentiful and highly digestible, and the 'missed' paddocks are cut for silage, whether or not there is other silage being made on the farm. Silage-making becomes a 'little and often' process from the paddocks, although of course other areas not normally grazed are also used. This system, together with irrigation, almost guarantees a good supply of grass. There is a rule that no area is grazed more than twice, without it being cut for silage, and the fouling effect is minimised and the need for topping completely eliminated.

Professor Holmes has adopted a different system. Four paddocks only are used, each being subdivided into seven, with a temporary electric fence. Each paddock lasts the cows one week. On Day One of the week they get one-seventh of the paddock area, on Day Two the original one-seventh plus a further seventh, resulting in the herd having the whole area on the seventh day. The cows move on to the next paddock, and this process is repeated over the next week.

At Wye 1,068 gallons of milk per acre (11,997 litres per hectare) were sold off this experimental area in a 20-week period. No topping is done or is necessary, but in direct contrast to Mr Morrey, there is no alternation of grazing and cutting.

Two systems with good results, in the hands of two experts, and always it is difficult to reconcile their differences. At the Hannah Research Institute at Ayr, Dr Malcolm Castle has attempted to compare set stocking with the Wye College System with the following results:

Set stocking = 1,030 gallons per acre (11,564 litres per hectare).
Wye College system = 1,120 gallons per acre (12,560 litres per hectare).

We need to find many more answers, which in turn will produce a new set of questions. Grazing systems for cows will vary according to the farm situation, the weather, the designed stocking rate, use of fertiliser, and of course the expertise and ability of the man in charge.

Chapter 6

WINTER FEEDING

As a grassland enthusiast I have chosen to discuss winter feeding before moving on to deal with the feeding of the herd at grass. There are very good reasons for this, as there is no doubt that the winter period is the most expensive period of the year, and although the price of milk is as yet not commensurate with this high cost, it is a very important part of the milk producer's year.

I will confine the discussion to herds that have to be housed in winter. By design, or by being blessed with favourable soil and climatic conditions, a few herds manage to winter outside in Britain, but a visit to two of these in January 1974 made one feel sorry for cows and cowmen alike. A New Zealander, without visiting the United Kingdom cannot comprehend the need for housing, and indeed after a few weeks in New Zealand in 1973, I was almost brainwashed myself into doubting the need for winter housing. My return just before Christmas 1973 soon convinced me why our cows were inside.

There must be thousands of combinations of methods of feeding dairy cows in winter. To follow each method would take far longer than this book could allow, even if I was foolish enough to claim that I had come across every method used. The winter feeding of the dairy cow has been given more attention than any other class of stock, and these studies are far more numerous and comprehensive than the studies of cows' requirements, and intakes at grass in summer.

We are all familiar with a sheet of paper received from our Ministry adviser or feedstuff or fertiliser agent giving the results of analysis of our silage or hay. The question is, however, how many of us understand this information sufficiently, and how often this is shrouded by vague scientific terms and figures, particularly their incomprehensible abbreviations, which seem to change regularly as if a secret code was necessary in case that one day we might understand it!

Grass products form the basis of winter feed for most dairy herds, although one must not forget that the arable farmers can use many arable by-products such as beet tops, good barley straw, stockfeed potatoes, pea haulm and maize silage, all of which often add up to good rations and higher milk yields in the east of England than in the west. It is strange to realise that the advantages of silage as a basis for winter feed as compared with hay have been preached in earnest since 1947, and we still have 70 per cent of our winter feed conserved as hay. A few years like 1974 will speed up this process, especially in the western half of the country.

SILAGE AS A BASIS OF FEEDING

The forage harvester has made a very major contribution in convincing farmers to make silage, but the relatively new introduction of the forage pick-up cart, similar to those used on the Continent, will mean a far more rapid move towards silage, particularly as this system can be used successfully and relatively rapidly in a one- or two-man situation, or more importantly on steeper land. I would go as far as to predict that there will be as many of these machines in the west in five years as there are now balers.

This book is not meant to discuss the advantages of silage, as compared with hay-making, in easing the management of grassland in summer; suffice to say that in 1974 silage-makers were cutting a second crop, or grazing for the second time after cutting, while hay men were still confronted with ancient mature rubbish, or worse still trying in vain to dry, half-rotten hay. Recovery of the sward after this treatment was very slow indeed, compared to the rapid recovery of swards cut more frequently for silage, and unless there was a very low stocking rate, it was impossible to provide a continuous supply of grass suitable for the grazing milking cow.

THE NUTRITIVE NEEDS OF THE COW

To return to the winter, and to enumerate the needs of the cow is fairly simple:

1. Energy.　　　　　　　4. Vitamins.
2. Protein.　　　　　　　5. Water.
3. Minerals.

But we have to equate this seemingly very simple list to a cow's ration and to feeds available on the farm, taking into consideration the quantity and quality of the feed.

Although the data which I shall refer to are available in many other publications, it is necessary to discuss them as a basis for winter feeding.

Unfortunately, a cow's needs have been split into two categories: *maintenance* and *production* requirements. This has been done of course merely for ease of calculation. It is very misleading, as it gives

7. Cutting good quality grass for making wilted silage (Frondeg, 1975).

8. Picking up high quality wilted grass for silage. Chopping aids fermentation and increases intake (Frondeg, 1975).

the impression that there is a two-way 'gate', similar to that at the end of a sheep race, shedding feed two ways, one towards maintaining the cow's body, respiration, movement, heat, and repair of body cells, etc, and the residue towards manufacturing milk in the case of the milking cow or building up reserves and supplying the needs of the developing calf in the case of a pregnant cow.

These calculations of maintenance and production requirements are merely a very convenient way of expressing the cow's theoretical feed requirement. The danger is that we think that a two and a half gallon (11·4 litre) cow on moderate self-feed silage gets her maintenance requirement from the 100 lb (45·3 kg) or so of silage that she is eating, and that the 10 lb (4·53 kg) of concentrates she is getting is wholly responsible for her milk.

The fact is that this cow will probably milk 2 gallons (9·1 litres) or more if all her concentrates were cut off (which they probably should be). She will eat more silage to compensate for the loss of concentrates, in this case, of course, concentrates, as they so often are, are not being used to supplement roughage, but actually to replace it when we look at the cow's total diet.

This cow will sometimes make available the nutrients necessary 'off her back' if the silage is not good enough, or for various reasons, such as restrictions at the face, the cow is not able to get enough. This milking off her back must be watched in relation to the stage of lactation. It happens quite normally in the early part of the lactation, but later in the lactation this loss of weight should be corrected as the effects may not be immediately apparent. Poor condition will contribute later to a poor start to the next lactation, poor conception, and, as is happening in some herds, to a condition described as a 'lean cow syndrome' (with apologies to the pig farmer for the nomenclature).

FEED PER GALLON

It is important to mention and discuss the increasing gradation in feed requirement per gallon with increased yields. We have often referred to 4 lb per gallon (0·4 kg per litre) cake without thinking, as if it was as easy to get the seventh gallon (31·8 litres) as it was the first. If we compare the cow (merely as an example, although the non-supporters of the Friesian breed will be delighted with the description) to a large wet sponge from which we are extracting as much water as possible, the energy required to squeeze out the first half pint is relatively little, to get the last possible drop will require enormous energy.

In exactly the same way we need more feed per gallon (per litre), to produce the sixth, than the first, and similarly as we go higher up the scale, towards seven, eight or nine gallons (31·8, 36·3 or 40·9 litres) per day, not only is the actual feed input important, but when, how, and how often it is fed becomes more important. Alternative wet and dry feeds, and its palatability, become very important as any herdsman in charge of a high-yielding herd will tell you, or will tell you in part, retaining a few of his secrets of success up his sleeve.

THE COW'S NEEDS DURING LACTATION

Let us return now to see how the cow's requirements can be met during the winter period.

Before Calving

It is very noticeable in any herd, fed good silage, and calving between January and March, how quickly after drying off the cows put on flesh. Mr Gwynant Edwards, of Nantisiriol, near Aberystwyth, had one of the best silage clamps I have ever seen in the 1974/75 winter. It had a good analysis: 31 per cent dry matter and a starch equivalent of 55 per cent and a pH of 3·9; it looked good, smelled good, and was short chopped and easily available at the self feed face, and this feeding face itself had no waste whatsoever, and was perfectly vertical. His in-calf cows, mainly calving in January and February, put on flesh at a dramatic rate on silage alone.

There were no details of the actual liveweight of the cows. This merely shows that good, well-made silage can be a very good pre-calving ration for cows, possibly supplemented in the last few weeks as the appetite and silage intake of the cows is depressed to a large extent by the physical size of the calf reducing the effective size of the rumen.

We are not always able to achieve this type of clamp, and then supplementary feeding may be necessary. Cows must be fit, not fat, before calving if a good lactation is to be obtained.

The First Five Weeks of a Lactation

A good stockman will reduce concentrate feeding substantially a few days before calving, so that the cow does not get 'fogged up'. A symptom of this is scouring after calving. Nor is it good stockmanship to present a newly calved cow with a full ration of concentrates. Calving is a traumatic experience with both hormonal and physical changes taking place.

On average, cows take about five weeks to reach peak production if conditions are right. However, it is of no use expecting high peak yields on wet, rubbishy silage and little or no concentrates. During this period, it is good practice to 'lead feed', at a rate of input about half a gallon (2·27 litres) in excess of the cow's current requirements, thereby making sure that lack of nutrients is in no way acting as a limiting factor to achieving maximum peak yield. A cow yielding $4\frac{1}{2}$ gallons (20·5 litres) in December in her second week of lactation needs every opportunity to achieve her potential maximum, as it is this maximum that often governs the total lactation yield.

Five Weeks to Twelve Weeks

By this time the cow should be settling down and often the 'lead feed' can be discontinued, feeding strictly according to yield. Cows that achieve high yields at any time and are getting a large quantity of concentrates must be watched very carefully. Little and often is the key word to feeding these cows during this period if this is possible, and not trying to get an enormous quantity into the cow at milking time only. I have found the provision of feed mangers in the yard a great advantage towards feeding the cow at this time of lactation.

Twelve to Twenty-four Weeks

The cow is now on the 'plateau' part of her lactation, and here more use can be made of roughage. By this period, the cow's appetite is normally at its greatest, she is able to take in more hay or silage in quantities that seemed vast to many farmers who were short of fodder in the spring of 1975, but one redeeming fact is that the cow's system can make maximum use of silage or hay at this time, whereas in the previous period of the lactation a basic self feed allowance of silage may have provided maintenance only. In this three month period, from the third to the sixth month of lactation, economies of feed are possible compared with early lactation. Some silage will give M + 1, $1\frac{1}{4}$ or even 2 gallons (4·5, 6·8 or even 9·0 litres) but rarely above this unless the quality is exceptionally good. This period is also the time for serving the cows. Underfeeding before or during this period can be critical in relation to actual heat detection and conception. For the first three months or so a good cow will lose considerable flesh, and depending of course on the feed regime, she will begin to put flesh on slowly in the next three months. Work at Liverpool University has shown that a cow actually losing flesh and weight when served is far more likely not to conceive than a cow that is just beginning to put on weight at service.

Good conception and a resultant good calving index of around 360–380 days is a highly important factor in determining profitability, and of course is also vital in maintaining the herd's calving pattern, that is, if one had been adopted.

Twenty-four Weeks to Drying Off

All winter-calving cows are at grass at this stage, and the only comment I make is that however good we think our feed and feeding system, is spring grass always gives that magic boost to yields at turnout—the earlier the turnout, the more valuable the result—as a substantial quantity of milk can be produced in early spring off grass at winter prices. This boost in milk is, I always suspect, not simply nutritional. Every year we have a few cows in March with acetonaemia (slow fever) symptoms of which can be treated by the vet. Cows giving in excess of six gallons (27·3 litres) will suddenly look hollow, starey coated and will give less than two gallons (9·1 litres) a day. Veterinary treatment will allow a return of milk to four or even five gallons (18·2 or 22·7 litres) a day, but it is not until they get grass that they really recover, their bloom returns, and we are back to the six-gallon (27·3 litres) yields again.

If one cow in the herd is diagnosed to have clinical acetonaemia there will be ten with sub-clinical symptoms. I think that grass in spring causes these cows to recover and transform the five-gallon (22·7 litres) sub-clinical acetonaemia cow to a six-gallon (27·3 litres) healthy cow.

HIGH YIELDS, HIGH MARGINS?

Here I have described a system based on the herd relying to a maximum extent in winter on grass products and other arable products, with supplementary feed being given as concentrates. Let me correct any thoughts you may have that every cow in the country is fed in this way. We will have to disregard the farmer who is always in trouble through lack of fodder or other mis-management. It is worth considering the men who deliberately underfeed, whose level of feeding means that a cow with a six-gallon (27·3 litres) potential peaks at four gallons (18·2 litres), but the truth is that this system is often as profitable, in terms of margin over concentrates, as many other systems where high feeding is practised. This is shown by the following examples, taking milk at 32p per gallon (7·4p per litre) and concentrates at £80 per ton (£81 per tonne):

Herd	Gallons sold per cow per year	Concentrate use	Margin over concentrates
A	750 gall (3405 l) (£240)	3 cwt (152 kg) (£12)	£228
B	1000 gall (4540 l) (£320)	23 cwt (1168 kg) (£92)	£228
C	1300 gall (5902 l) (£416)	47 cwt (2387 kg) (£188)	£228

Pride is swallowed, in that the low producer will have to quote a yield of 700–800 gallons (3,182–4,091 litres) rather than upwards of

1,200 gallons (5,454 litres) per cow, but if economics demand this, and he is left with a satisfactory margin, and eventually profit, all is well. This is provided that there are no long-term effects of low level feeding that will eventually catch up with him such as low conception rates, etc. A remark made by Giles Tedstone, a 220-cow dairy farmer in the Wirral was: 'Feeding concentrates to cows only results in reducing your margin over concentrates'. This is a statement to think about seriously. I do not think it is true in all situations, but the concept that he is implying in his usual inimitable way, of getting more milk from basic fodder and grazing, is very valid. Many, however, cannot and do not want to swallow pride. Thank goodness that achieving high yields, provided they are economical, is still a constant joy to many farmers, herdsmen and farm managers. Without this the milk-producing industry would very quickly fall to that of factory process levels and bring with it all the job dissatisfaction that this implies.

MORE USE OF SILAGE

Let us hope that in time the diet of the vast majority of our dairy cows in winter will be based on silage, and that the present national trend in producing a vastly better quality silage, compared to that of a few years ago, will be maintained.

The practice of cutting earlier, wilting and the use of additives when necessary have been major contributing factors to making better quality silage. It is important to realise that cutting earlier (before, or at, flower head emergence) enables highly digestible silage to be made. What this means in simple terms is that a higher proportion of the food eaten can be digested and pass in soluble, usable form from the animal's gut into the blood stream. With highly digestible silage also, there is a second desirable effect. The comparatively lower 'load' of undigested fibre does not clog up the cow's digestive tract, but passes through the digestive system more quickly, and maintains the cow's appetite, resulting in a cow eating more, and this in turn enables more reliance to be put on the silage constituent of the ration towards production.

THE USE OF GOOD HAY

In exactly the same way, successful cow-feeding based on hay depends on the stage of cutting. Well-made early hay is far better than well made late hay in terms of digestibility, a phenomenon that farmers have always been aware of in that early hay seems to be consumed far more quickly than late made hay. Normally, the best early hay is kept until last, and of course unless carefully rationed, it very quickly disappears, causing anxious days, particularly in a late spring.

A very good indicator of the digestibility and value of hay is the consistency of the dung; normally the firmer the dung, the more fibre remains undigested, indicating the low digestibility of the hay.

If a farm has to resort to haymaking because of constraints of land steepness or accessibility with a forage harvester, or through personal choice, then the use of a cold air blower to achieve a consistently good product is almost a necessity. Good, early cut, barn dried hay is an excellent feed for milk production.

TIME OF CALVING

A discussion on winter feeding is complicated enough because of the vast number of feeds involved, but this of course is further complicated, and the permutations achieve football pool levels when we consider the various calving patterns of a herd.

The system of calving cows in early autumn offers many advantages; calving can take place outside, and the grass in early autumn can be responsible for a fair amount of milk production, particularly if the weather is not too wet. Cows and heifers calving at this time have been steamed up on grass very successfully and are usually very fit. Tony McHarg, of Frizington Park in West Cumbria, calves all his herd in August, and I have never seen such a fit herd as his at this time of year. One word of warning, however—the danger of the susceptibility of the heifers in particular to summer mastitis, a cruel disease that can cause irreparable damage to a group of heifers, usually striking the most promising ones, the daughters of your best cows by an expensive nominated sire.

VALUE OF AUTUMN GRASS

After calving it is a serious mistake to expect the grass available, no matter how good it seems, to support a cow milking six to seven gallons (27 to 31 litres). The problem is that many cows will produce this level on grass alone, but often the loss of body weight and condition is so rapid and dramatic that it is impossible to maintain a good level of production later, and it will often be difficult to get the cows in calf again at the right time to maintain a good calving index and calving pattern.

Two-and-a-half gallons (11·4 litres) of milk in September and two gallons (9·1 litres) in October is ample, and if lead feeding is practised at this time, then one-and-a-half gallons and one gallon (6·8 and 4·5 litres) for each month is sufficient. Gradual introduction to winter fodder during October is necessary, making sure that this transition is slow to allow the rumen bacteria to change from bacteria capable of dealing with a mainly grass diet, to those capable of working on whatever winter diet the cows are on.

USE OF KALE

Many cows calving in August, September and October, particularly into eastern Britain rely heavily on kale, which is an excellent feed for dairy cows provided it can be utilised, and this means having relatively dry land. Kale also becomes very important as often grass growth, due to drought, stops very much earlier in the east than in the west. On visits to the south east in early autumn, one is always amazed that cows are feeding on kale so early, often together with such luxuries (in the west) as good barley straw, brewers' grains and recently green fed or even strip-grazed maize. Later, sugar-beet tops form a successful part of the ration.

Relying too heavily on kale in the ration can be dangerous. There is ample evidence that kale can cause infertility in cows at the very time that the herd is being bulled.

CALVING BOXES

I may be paying undue attention to the point that calving in autumn can take place in the open. Unless there is any trouble, this is best in a paddock near the steading. Conditions there are usually far more sterile than in a box, and the danger of the cow slipping is eliminated as compared to calving in a concrete area, unless there is a very good layer of strawy muck in the box. I am very aware of the number of boxes and straw yards required for a herd calving in January and February, and a herdsman at this time is always looking for more boxes, and carefully looking at the whole herd frequently, to prevent any calving in cubicles, which can be dangerous to calf and dam.

STEAMING UP OR NOT?

The pattern of feeding necessary to get cows fit for calving and able to milk off their backs will vary enormously in winter calvers. If the silage or hay is very good, and there is a plentiful supply of fodder, dry cows in November and December will put flesh on very rapidly, and there is no need to think of steaming up except perhaps for the last two to three weeks. Many producers have been mistaken at this period in thinking that late winter/spring calvers need only

9. Kale strip grazed in autumn is a valuable feed.

10. An open clamp is quite satisfactory for winter feeding provided it is in a fairly sheltered position.

rough stemmy silage or hay. The cows usually come off grass fairly lean, as they have been producing two to three gallons (9·1 to 13·6 litres) off grass which is often wet and of low feed value, and cows, particularly the young cows, lose flesh very rapidly at this time of year. If the silage or hay is not good, the cows who are getting little or usually no concentrates, will not put flesh on, and a cow in a lean condition is in a poor state for the start of her next lactation.

If the silage or hay is not good, a six-week steaming-up programme is essential. A programme of 2 lb per day (0·9 kg), building up to 12 lb (5·4 kg) per day, of a mainly cereal ration can usually result in the cow calving down in good condition and full of milk. It must not be forgotten that this uses about 3 cwt (150 kg) of concentrates, but well worth while providing that feeding after calving is adequate.

A very similar programme of feeding is needed for cows calving in March and April, but here turnout normally coincides with peak yields and from mid-May concentrate feeding can be stopped at this point, provided the grassland management is good. Cows calving during this period usually have a relatively short lactation as they dry off when the quality of feed declines in autumn, unless one feeds concentrates at this late part of the lactation which usually gives a very uneconomic response.

FEEDING METHODS

The introduction of self-feeding silage on a large scale has revolutionised cow management in winter. To many of us the cutting and carting of bulky silage around a cowshed are thankfully just an unpleasant memory.

Of course, as always, and comparable to the development of the tractor, many farmers immediately made a relatively cheap and easy system more complicated. I became a victim of tombstone barriers, and then modified tombstone barriers, built as I thought to withstand an attack by a Centurion tank. With a herd of cows, we must never underestimate their strength and destructive potential. Constant repairs, together with bruised shoulders (both man and beast) and the difficulty of removing waste from the silage face, have thankfully banished tombstone barriers to rot in stockyards, hidden from sight, at least in the summer, by beds of nettles.

The lethal property of these barriers is an equally important reason for their disuse, as many a cow lost its life by being guillotined by a silage landslide on her neck. The use of high tensile electrified barbed wire, or light wire rope, is ideal for use as a barrier and can be lifted up or down at will to guide the cow's eating position and maintain a tidy face. Provided the silage is good, and particularly if it is of even quality and, fermentation, very good clean vertical walls can be maintained up to 7′ 6″ (2·3 m) in height. If the silage has bad pockets, or layers, with poor fermentation, this can often be due to soil contamination. If the face is not tended every day, cows can easily burrow into the face or leave layers, which can be dangerous in that this can cause a fatal fall of silage.

I have always been a little unhappy with a self-feeding system. With a good clamp, labour requirement is low and the system works well. The problem arises when the silage is not so good, or variable in quality, and considerable effort is needed to maintain a good face, not to mention the actual waste of material. This can be overcome by holding the cows back until they are hungry enough to produce a good silage face, but this is not good for efficient milk production.

COW'S TEETH

Problems arise with the animal's ability to extract the silage from the self-feed face. Young cows changing teeth is one problem group, and a second group consists of old cows with worn or missing teeth, and ample evidence of both can be found if we look carefully, as lost teeth can often be found on the floor of the feeding area. It is hard enough for a first calver or an old cow to compete for her feed with a hundred or more herd mates; the added handicap of missing teeth and sore gums is often the cause of very lean heifers and old cows in winter.

The length of chop can of course modify the ease of eating at the face. A precision chop machine capable of chopping to $\frac{3}{4}$″–1″ (19–25·4 mm) cannot be justified or afforded by many farmers. A double chop, kept sharp and giving 3″–6″ (76–152 mm) chop, can provide a fairly easily fed silage compared with completely unchopped silage. The degree of consolidation, and the related height of the clamp, can affect ease of extraction and must also be borne in mind.

I have always wanted to put up an easy feed system to suit cows, cowman and the pocket alike. There is no doubt that the intake of high yielders can be increased by easy feeding; there is less energy expended in feeding, more time to lie down and to chew the cud and also, particularly for the shyer cow, more time allowed for eating.

The system has problems. A 2′–2′ 3″ length (610–686 mm) per cow is required, as cows are all expected to eat at once, after replenishing the mangers and after milking, which are the peak feeding times. This compared with 9″ or even 6″ (229 or 152 mm) face at a self feeding face, although I have always maintained that 6″ (152 mm) per cow is very much on the tight side for cows in full milk production.

A CHEAP EASY-FEED SYSTEM

Without wanting to start too long an argument about feeding methods, the use of a forage box is the obvious choice. A good mechanic, however, must not be too far away from this machine, especially on Sunday mornings! The use of a very simple system as we use at Frondeg, based on a fore-end loader, means that no extra expensive equipment other than that already on the farm need be bought; there are seldom breakdowns, and if it did, another can be borrowed from a neighbour fairly easily.

The 7' (2·1 m) wide passage, with angled cow divisions (as seen in photo 11) allows 2' 6" (762 mm) per cow for feeding, and permits the majority of concentrates to be fed in the passage, cutting down on parlour feeding enormously and enabling us to feed a variety of rations. In the parlour of course one is normally restricted to one type of feed only. A basic cereal based ration can be fed at the feed face and cubes in the parlour. The time allowed in a quick throughput parlour is normally hardly long enough for eating the required amount of concentrates in winter.

I cannot imagine that our newly calved heifers are any different from the majority of heifers, but many of ours owing to nervousness of new surroundings often refuse to eat feed in the parlour until they have settled down. Relying on feeding all concentrates in the parlour will mean that this type of heifer is being severely underfed at this critical time. We can compensate, in part at least, for this by giving these heifers the bulk of their concentrate ration at a feed fence outside the parlour where they can eat their ration more in their own time.

I have concentrated here on clamp silage feeding, by far the most important. I have never been convinced of the economic advantage of a tower silo installation, although of course I realise that apart from costs and maintenance requirements, it is a more sophisticated system and in the right hands can produce extremely good fodder for milk production. For the farmer who can justify and afford such a system, savings in wastage and concentrate bills can be very large and provided he or his men are mechanically minded, he can enjoy the advantages of automation.

The advantages of using a feed manger, described previously, are all enjoyed as well, and of course mechanical feeding systems can ease both silage and concentrate feeding, or an integral mixture of both.

As each of the operators of these systems will know, the resultant feed value of the silage that comes out is dependent on the grass or other forage put in. High dry matter is essential or the machinery for

11. Farm-built feed barriers at Frondeg Farm. Easy feeding allows for more control of silage intake.

extraction will often fail. High dry-matter also almost guarantees good fermentation.

The problem of answering the question, 'How much silage do I need for the winter period' is always one that we must consider carefully. This answer depends on the type of system, alternative methods of feeding, etc, but more important on the amount of dry matter available.

A clamp of 1,000 tons (1,000 tonnes) at 20 per cent dry matter will have 200 tons (200 tonnes) dry matter, while a clamp of 30 per cent will have 300 tons (300 tonnes) or a 50 per cent increase. If an average cow consuming 25 lb (11·2 kg) dry matter as silage per day is considered, over a 150-day winter she will need 3,750 lb (1,685 kg) of dry matter. This represents 8 tons (8 tonnes) of 20 per cent dry matter silage, or only 5·3 tons (5·3 tonnes) of 30 per cent dry matter silage. In many instances, particularly when a cow is in calf, the physical amount of water she has to ingest creates a filling effect, and often she will eat less. Coupled with this also is the fact that 20 per cent silage, especially in the lower layers of the silo, will often be of unsatisfactory fermentation, particularly butyric fermentation which again markedly reduces intake.

Chapter 7

HOUSING THE DAIRY HERD

IT IS DIFFICULT to imagine, that a few years ago most of our dairy cows were still tied by the neck, even in relatively large herds. The move to loose yarding of cows must have been welcomed by herdsmen, but more particularly by the cows themselves. The change presented its problems; unless a large quantity of straw was available, cows became very dirty. Sufficient room, about 100–120 square feet (9·3–11·1 sq m) per cow for lying was essential, and provided these two main criteria were met, this was, and still is, a very satisfactory system.

Many systems were designed to improve loose housing. The use of the bed and breakfast system with cows lying in a thick bed of sawdust on top of a silage clamp was very successful, particularly in Cumberland, but was labour consuming and expensive as sawdust and haulage became more costly. A few slatted floor systems were designed for cows, but there are probably no two more miserable sights than dairy cows on slats and a cowman trying to clean these cows' udders for milking. Slatted floor systems brought with them a saving of straw, but also dirty cows with trodden teats, chilled udders and a mastitis problem. Needless to say their stay was thankfully short lived.

With loose housing came parlour milking, the fixed bail, the abreast, the tandem, and later the herringbone and rotary parlours in that order. More cows could be milked per man, a factor that has become increasingly more important as labour bills increased, but not as important as some people maintain. Cows per man hour is not the be all and end all. Efficient, clean disease-free milking, and getting the maximum yield per cow that the system will allow, should still be our main aims.

The most recent survey* showed that in 1974 there were still 68 per cent of all herds in the United Kingdom milked throughout the year in cowsheds, shippons, byres, cowhouses, cowstalls, or whatever other name they may be called in various parts of the country. Pipeline milking and efficient muck scrapers can make these units extremely

* E. E. C. Dairy Facts and Figures (1974) Economics Division, Milk Marketing Board.

efficient. Many a herd has been batch-milked very successfully through a cowshed, with a pipeline attached, during the period of its growth and before the increase in cow numbers had justified, or hopefully had generated enough capital to afford the next step in development, a new milking parlour.

THE DEVELOPMENT OF THE CUBICLE

In 1960 the pundits shook their heads knowingly as they witnessed the development of cubicle systems. That year saw a quick return to cowsheds, those who had retained their old cowshed systems proclaimed loudly that this step had to come. The only addition needed was a tie chain, or rope, and a manger and we would be back in square one. The advent of the cubicle was an exciting one, and caught on throughout the world very rapidly. The only advantage that the cowshed men enjoyed was that when they eventually joined the cubicle set, their cows were so much easier to train to use them.

Hywel Evans, then in Cheshire, and now farming in Anglesey, was responsible for the development of cubicles, and it must be extremely satisfying for him to think that the idea with which he experimented on a small scale should become a system used throughout the world for dairy cows, and even other classes of cattle.

Many variations of the basic design have of course been developed, but the simple original concept is still adhered to. I will not discuss here the relative lengths, position of cross bars, uprights, size of tube used, wooden or steel cubicles, or combinations of new or second-hand wood, steel and rope. These in themselves are sufficient for a book. As always, it is better to visit a few systems and see for oneself how they are working in practice.

The lengths and width of a cubicle have to be related to the breed or type of cow. The following sizes are normally used:

	Length		Width	
	ft. in.	(m)	ft. in.	(m)
British Canadian Holstein	7·3	(2·30)	4·0	(1·20)
British Friesian	6·9	(2·10)	3·9	(1·15)
Ayrshire, Guernsey	6·9	(2·10)	3·9	(1·15)
Jersey	6·6	(2·00)	3·6	(1·07)

However, I see difficulties immediately from quoting these figures. In any herd there are great variations in cow sizes. In a typical British Friesian herd, heifers will weigh from 930–1,000 lb (422–453 kg) at calving at two years, while mature in-calf fourth calvers may weigh up to 1,500–1,700 lb (780–790 kg).

When deciding on a size we have to take the mythical average cow, and cater for a cow substantially bigger than her. Small cows can live in big cubicles, even though they may also dung in them. Very large cows will not lie in small cubicles.

The Position of the Neck Rail

A neck rail is usually included in the design, to encourage cows to dung in the passages. A rail strategically placed can be of great help, but it must not hinder the cow when getting up or lying down. A rail about 2' 6" (760 mm) from the floor level inside the cubicle is usually satisfactory, as it allows the cow plenty of room to get up 'below' it but annoys her sufficiently after she has stood up, to make her stand back and dung in the passage, not in the cubicle.

I have spent many hours deciding where to place this neck rail. One way of assessing if it is right is by observing the cows, particularly in the night. One will soon see whether they are experiencing difficulty in getting up and down at this time as there is little else to disturb them. There is no need to fix all the neck rails at once. Fixing 15 to 20 rails is sufficient and whilst observing these, one will soon see whether they are effective in keeping cubicles clean. Of course one sure way of assessing whether they are a hindrance to the herd is if very few cows use these cubicles over a period of a few days. This is a sure sign that a move of the rail is necessary. I have never fixed a neck rail in a new cubicle set-up until the cows have settled down over at least a month. During this time the herd needs all the persuasion you can give, although this may have one other disadvantage—without a rail some old cows will lie too far forward and will, especially if they are heavy in calf, find it difficult to get up if they are lying too close to the front, particularly in a cubicle attached to a wall.

Cow comfort is most important with cubicles. Cows which associate getting hurt with the use of cubicles—pain caused by bruising hook bones, ribs or hocks—will be reluctant to use them and will lie in the passage or the feeding face. These cows become extremely filthy in a very short time and are almost impossible to re-train. Some cows will adopt a half in half out position, which must be the most uncomfortable method of lying they can find, as the heelstone is poking into their ribs, and of course, in this position they are very prone to teat damage by being trodden on.

Thankfully, in most herds there are relatively few non-takers of cubicles. Not so good ones are best got rid of, preferably as barreners so that no other farmer inherits your problems. Good cows can often be found a comfortable box to lie in, provided there are only one or two such offenders.

Cubicle floor design has probably attracted more attention than any other facet of this system. Rammed clay or chalk make good beds but need attention often as, with constant use, holes and unevenness can develop in the floor.

The first design I refer to is the Newton Rigg type, designed to hold sawdust or straw but allowing a fall for the drainage of urine. The second is the very commonly used sleeper on edge, with a retaining edge for bedding. Unfortunately, this edge is often responsible for retaining dung and, unless cleaned often will result in dirty cows. The third type has a plain floor with no heelstone shape and is, in my opinion, just as effective; dung is easily removed, urine does not collect, and with roughish concrete covered with sawdust, it makes a very good, easily maintained cubicle.

Bedding the Cubicle

Various types of bedding materials are used. Whilst sawdust is excellent, it is difficult to get in many areas and is sometimes blamed for causing teat soreness and subsequent mastitis, although I have no evidence to support this. Where available, long straw is excellent and provides a very comfortable bed. If dung is handled semi-solid, the effect of cows drawing long straw into the dung passage is good as it mixes and makes the material easy to handle. However, the converse is true if the system is designed to handle semi-liquid slurry. Chopped straw is probably the best of all bedding materials. It combines comfort and warmth, and being chopped, cannot be drawn out to any extent into the slurry passage. If it is, it does not interfere with flow, pumps, etc, to the extent that long straw does.

You may, however, wonder where the chopping machinery or chaff cutter of yesterday is to come from, to chop this straw. There is a ready-made alternative in many farms—the precision chop forage harvester, which will not only chop the straw, but also blow it conveniently for storage purposes, provided a 'sack stocking' is made to divert the chopped material to the right place.

It is a relatively easy matter to adapt a farm trolley, by adding high sides, to transport the straw to the cubicles. Time used in shaking out straw into cubicles is eliminated, and chopping can result in the saving of considerable quantities of straw over the winter period.

The most positive contribution made by a cubicle system is in the saving of straw, coupled with the maintenance of very clean cows, provided, as with any other system, there is sufficient attention given to detail. With the astronomical increase in straw prices, particularly in the west, in the last few years, it is little wonder that cubicles have become even more popular.

Young Stock in Cubicles

For the last three years at Frondeg, all our dairy young stock that are housed, and are over nine months of age, are housed in cubicles. January- and February-born heifer calves, housed in October, have cubicles measuring 3' 0" wide and 5' 6" long (915 mm by 1,680 mm). This size is a little large for their age, but this in itself is an advantage in that we have no trouble in getting the calves to use the cubicles, especially if we do not scrape the slurry away for the first two or three days but provide ample bedding in the cubicles themselves. In every case up to now the heifers have quickly responded and obviously prefer a clean dry bed, rather than to lie in 3" to 4" (75 to 100 mm) of slurry in the passages.

By turnout in April these heifers are 15 months old and the cubicles fit them perfectly. Needless to say, there are no problems in succeeding winters in getting calved heifers to use cubicles, as they have adopted the habit at a very early age.

How Many Cubicles per Cow?

One cubicle per heifer, or heifer calf, is allowed as they invariably lie down together, the peak times being mid-day and midnight. With a herd of cows of course, particularly with a self-feed or easy feed system, one can get away quite successfully with 85–90 per cent of cubicles in relation to the total number of cows. There are again peak periods of lying down, but there are invariably 10 to 15 per cent of cows eating or just loafing around, chewing their cud. Eighty-five to ninety cubicles will easily cater for a herd of a hundred cows.

Many loose housing systems built before 1970 were designed with integrated and adjacent silage and lying areas. Buildings with spans of between 45' and 120' (13·7–36·5 m) emerged, with of course related heights. This height was required to accommodate silage before it settled, plus a tractor and buckrake on top when filling. This space was later conveniently used for straw storage.

The bedded areas, often lean-tos to the main silo, were also usually very high, to allow for ventilation. This was in the era before the widespread reintroduction of the most efficient space boards or Yorkshire boarding. This height was demanded by the density of the cows in the building and added enormously to the cost of these buildings.

COW KENNELS

The development of cow kennels, with their low roofs and open ridge ventilation, has been almost as exciting as the development of the cubicle itself. A kennel system, together with an open clamp silo with railway sleeper walls, provided an excellent and relatively cheap system, especially suited to an expanding herd which is the position that most dairy farmers have found themselves in recent years.

It is sad, however, that with many of these package-deal kennel units a farmer did not choose, for a few pounds extra per cow housed, a building with slightly stronger timber fixed by means of bolts rather than nails. It would, I am certain, have paid him handsomely in a relatively short time, in the saving of time and materials necessary to maintain these buildings. After two to three years, with the cheaper buildings it is common practice to go the rounds every morning with hammer and nails, and also often with replacement timber.

COW MOVEMENT

Milking parlours, and the work routines within them, will be discussed in Chapter 10. Here I want to deal with work routines and the movement of cows and feeding systems in and around the feeding area, and of course ease of gathering cows as a whole or as a group into the collecting yard, and their dispersal after milking.

I have never had the opportunity of designing, setting up and working a new set-up from scratch, but have always had to fit a system into existing buildings, which in itself is very interesting and rewarding. Mr Graham Stewart, Bowden Park Farm, Lacock, Wiltshire, and once my neighbour, has had the opportunity not only of modifying a system to milk 200 cows, but also of designing another 120-cow set-up from bare ground. This new set-up is, in my opinion, one of the most efficient and easily-worked units I have seen. (See photo 12 and fig 3.) Some of the reasons that make this unit so efficient are given below:

1. Cows are divided into four units of thirty. They can therefore be fed at the feeding face, allowing 2' 3" (690 mm) per cow according to yield, stage of lactation, etc. Very good silage is of course given to the highest yielding group, and similarly recently dried cows, or nearly dry cows, can be fed with silage of inferior quality. By using the forage box, cows can also be given a varied diet, using grass silage once per day and maize silage the opposite end of the day, especially again for high yielders. Variety, in my opinion, undoubtedly increases intake, no matter how good the feed is.
2. Division of cows into smaller groups decreases stress; this also enables young cows or heifers to be separated from the more mature cows.
3. Slurry areas can be scraped simply by moving cows through wide gateways again minimising stress.
4. Cows are easily diverted for veterinary attention or AI. Special cubicles with back chains are available to hold these cows. They are not removed from the main building and their herd mates,

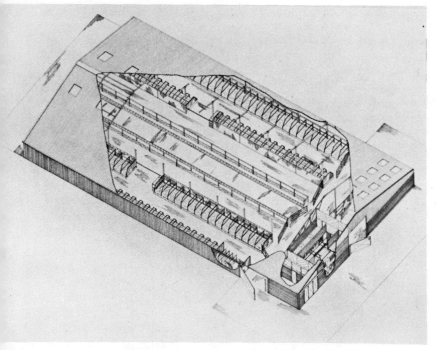

12. Artist's impression of 118-cow Hosier 'Hilton' House at Bowden Park Farm, Lacock, Wiltshire, as shown in fig. 3.
Ack: Hill Hosier Ltd., Eastleigh, Southampton.

again decreasing stress.

[It is most important in any parlour set-up that two exits are available so that cows can be easily diverted as they leave the parlour for veterinary attention, or service. This arrangement can easily be incorporated into the system. It is far more difficult and time-consuming to sort out individual cows from a mob of 100 after they have left the parlour. It is far better for cows not wanted for attention to return to their grazing immediately after milking than stand about in the yard.]

5. All cows can be easily seen—also important for good herdsmanship. The system encourages the herdsman to walk up and down between the cows, and gives him every opportunity to observe his cows.

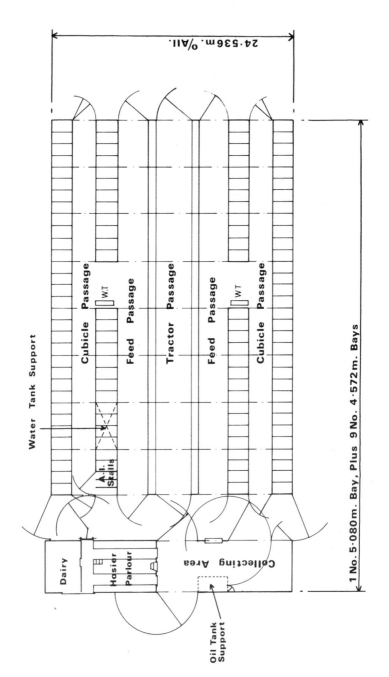

Fig. 3. Hosier 'Hilton' House for 118 cows.
Ack. Hill Hosier Ltd, Eastleigh, Southampton

6. The collecting yard is large enough to prevent stress, and the entrance to the milking parlour is directly in front of the cows which results in very easy movement in and out of the parlour. Groups can be easily collected and returned to their quarters by single gate combinations.
7. The slurry is easily handled into a primary reception tank, and is easily removed by fore-end loader without requiring expensive equipment.
8. Cows, fed by forage box, are disturbed the minimum amount. The cost of a forage box is fully justified in that around 800 cattle are also fed on this farm.

This unit has proved to be remarkably efficient, with cows clean and quiet. Conditions are conducive to efficient and profitable milk production when the herd settles down.

This system cost £203 gross per cow in 1974 including parlour and all ancillary equipment. Forty per cent grant was available then, which reduced the cost per cow to £121. With escalating costs I dare not predict current costs for 1976–1980, but at the time, this system was reasonably priced and the expenditure involved was fully justified.

A Pole Barn Cubicle Unit

We do not all have sufficient capital, however, to call in a contractor and build a system such as Graham Stewart's. Photos 13 and 14 show a very much cheaper pole barn unit built at Frondeg in 1972/73. Although used for heifers, both calved and uncalved, is equally applicable to cow-keeping. If I were setting out to house a herd now, I would consider such a building very seriously, as it can be built in stages by labour on the farm, and this of course saves an enormous amount of money.

The photographs explain the building construction, and in fact, it is a 'pair' of 'lean-tos'. The centre passage with a $\frac{3}{4}''$ (19 mm) wire rope is ideal for a feed barrier (both silage and concentrates can be fed quickly and easily here) but it is not suitable for hay without providing Swedish hay boxes to prevent wastage. A building for 50 cows would measure 82' (24·9 m) by 42' (12·8 m) and here again cows can be grouped into four very easily. Yorkshire boards supply adequate ventilation; the 'ridge' formed by the overlap of the corrugated steel roof allows adequate air outlet, and the building is never cold.

Feeding is by means of a fore loader, once per day, and the silage can be 'teased' to each side each evening very easily.

In 1972 the cost of the building for 56 animals was £2,500 including a labour charge of £700. This is a total, without grant, of

£48 per animal housed. It can be put up surprisingly quickly. One starts by digging holes with an excavator, 'planting' the treated poles, fixing them in rammed soil, and then levelling the uprights off using a chainsaw to lop off the surplus heights of the poles, rather than the laborious method of adjusting by first finding a level base.

To many young farmers, and those in the process of expansion, this building has been most interesting. Students and visitors alike can see that they could tackle the erection of this building at home and save costs compared to buying a steel or concrete building. It also has the advantage in that you can increase its length quite easily as your herd numbers increase.

SLURRY: ITS VALUE, STORAGE AND DISPOSAL

Slurry on dairy farms has become an enormous and very often costly commodity or problem, depending on how you view the product. In 1975 the annual fertiliser value of slurry was £12 per cow, and therefore with such a high value as this, it is a commodity that must be stored and spread carefully to enable us to reap maximum value from its use.

As more and more cows have been housed in cublicles, and as individual herds have grown in size, more and more effort has had to be put into slurry handling and storage. Many weird, wonderful, and complicated systems have been and will be developed, involving pumps, squeezers, dehydrators, digestive systems—sufficient to attract 10,000 people to a slurry handling demonstration at Stoneleigh in March 1974.

In setting up or modifying any cow housing system, the first essential is to decide on one's method of handling and storage of slurry and then to build the system around this, rather than to attack the problem at a later date when it will almost certainly demand a high cost answer, often far greater than if the former method had been adopted.

The lagoon is probably the most common system used, unless of course the farm soil type and cropping allows the spreading of slurry every day, or every few days, directly on to the land. The lagoon is relatively cheap to excavate, and is fairly easily made provided that conditions are right (it is most important that there is a clay subsoil). It is worth putting at least a 9″ (228 mm) layer of hardcore on the floor, or even concrete, to allow for movement of tractors when emptying. Emptying methods can vary from a large grab shovel to the use of a tractor fore-loader. There is no doubt that considerable saving in equipment cost can be made within an area by the sharing of equipment between farms. For example, three or four neighbours

13. Exterior view of young stock building at Frondeg. Pole barn construction with space boarding.

14. Interior view of young stock building at Frondeg. After training in cubicles as yearlings, these animals always take to cubicles very easily throughout their lives.

who have a muck spreader each. One machine is essential on each farm, and sufficient for most of the year, but during the emptying of a lagoon these three spreaders can be brought together. Also, by doing this, they can justify hiring a large tractor shovel. During loading this machine travels less than a small tractor and causes less damage to the lagoon's floor and of course speeds up the operation dramatically. One must be careful, however, in any area that your co-operators are brucella free.

Many cubicle systems have slatted or gridded floors to the dung passages, which eliminates scraping, and the slurry (usually by means of sluice gates) flows naturally into a lagoon. The most expensive system to install, but not necessarily so in the long run, is the use of a modified silage tower circular base, to store slurry above ground. This system has one major advantage over all the others; there is no effluent or seepage problems, and provided the store is large enough, the operator is the master of his slurry problem, and not vice versa, as is all too often the case on many farms.

Chapter 8

BREEDING BETTER COWS

THE AIMS OF any breeding policy, whether we consider the Milk
Marketing Boards, commercial breeding companies, the pedigree
breeders or commercial breeders are the same. It is to produce cows
that will perform and produce to best advantage under the conditions
to which they are subjected. They will have a long productive life, be
easy to handle and convert feed supplied to them as efficiently as
possible into milk and therefore into money.

With the increasing reliance that we will have to put on forage
feeding, particularly feeding methods based on grass whether grazed
or conserved, an animal with a large rumen capable of taking aboard
a large quantity of feed and processing this efficiently into milk, is
necessary.

I have been very careful here not to say that a high yielding animal
is necessary. In many instances, indeed in most herds, individual
cows are not allowed to express their full potential for milk
production for good sound economic reasons. As an example, I will
mention a very good, highly profitable herd of Friesians averaging
750 gallons (3,409 litres) sold, but at the same time never receiving any
other food than grass or silage. A breeder of pedigree bulls must,
however, attain high yields as most of his customers, *as yet*, demand
that bull mothers must have high yields.

THE PEDIGREE BULL BREEDER

Many of our top pedigree breeders are well aware that these high
yields may be produced uneconomically under conditions removed
from those found in commercial practice. Until buyers accept the fact
that a 900-gallon (4,091 litre) cow receiving 3 cwt (153 kg) of concentrates a year may be of equal potential, and possibly more so, than
a 1,600-gallon (7,273 litre) cow receiving upwards of 3 tons (3·05
tonnes) of concentrates, the pedigree bull rearer, who after all relies on
his bull sales for income, will continue to practise this system. One
great danger if course is that the progeny of these bulls, whose dams
have been selected under high concentrate regimes, may not perform

at all well as milk producers in a commercial herd based mainly on grass. This may well be the reason why so few 'top' herd prefixes appear in our national Milk Marketing Boards' studs.

I have no quarrel with pedigree breeders. They have done a wonderful job in the last half century in improving the commercial value of our cattle. This is well demonstrated by the enormous improvement in udder conformation of the British Friesian, as an example. While the customer demands his product, the breeder, who must sell his cattle in competition with others, must produce these bulls as his business. One day, no doubt, a 1,000-gallon (4,546 litre) dam, having received 3 cwt (153 kg) of concentrates, will be perfectly acceptable as a bull mother provided she is of the right type and conformation and is milking in a herd averaging 800 gallons (3,630 litres) sold per annum.

AIMS OF BREEDING

Successful breeding can be summed up as having 'produced an efficient cow' in its widest possible context, producing a cow which is superior to its herd mates, in the following characteristics:

(1) Milk yield.
(2) Milk quality.
(3) Health.
(4) Fertility.
(5) Ease of handling and milking.
(6) Superior conformation related to production ability.
(7) Longevity and wearability.

I have not tried to list these seven points in order of importance. High heifer yields may be of little importance in a herd suffering from the ill effects of using a bad bull, where cows go off their feet as third calvers. High individual yields lose their importance if they are accompanied by low herd fertility and a calving index of 450 days, while the high yielding heifer that kicks off her milking unit seven times per milking is of little value in a large herd where speed of milking through a herringbone parlour is essential.

All the points listed are important, and of course if all seven were satisfied, we would have a near-perfect cow or herd. The aim of every breeder is to achieve and maintain as high a level of commercial characteristics as possible. High milk yields and high milk quality, in relation to the level of feed and management inputs, are important, but in looking at any of these figures, the conditions under which they were produced must be borne in mind.

Let us consider two cows, of very similar breeding in two separate herds. Cow 'A' has given 750 gallons (3,409 litres) of milk and her near relative, cow 'B', has given 1,100 gallons (5,000 litres) of milk, both as third calvers. Obviously if cow 'A' has milked in a herd where the other third calvers averaged 700 gallons (3,182 litres) she is a superior cow by 50 gallons (227 litres) over her contemporaries. Cow 'B's' herd mates as third calvers have averaged 1,250 gallons (5,682 litres), she is therefore a minus 150 gallons (681 litres) cow when compared with her contemporaries. It is therefore very difficult to compare these cows absolutely; suffice to say that considerable information is required before pronouncing which is a good or bad cow in each case.

MILK QUALITY

Of course milk quantity and quality are very much related. In general, but there are always many exceptions; high yielders tend to give milk of lower quality than low yielders, particularly in fat and protein content. This is not always the case, however, and it is the high yielder with high quality milk that we are looking for.

It is refreshing to remember that in New Zealand they never refer to milk yields as such, except for town milk suppliers. Milk produced per day, or per lactation, is always referred to as the number of pounds (kg) butterfat produced. In this way they combine milk yield and butterfat quality and will refer to a 400-lb (181 kg) butterfat cow, rather than a 1,000-gallon (4,546 litre) cow. The main aim of the majority of New Zealand dairy herds is of course butterfat production and they have adopted a system that gives them a figure denoting the true value of that animal to them.

If we take as our standard a 1,000-gallon (4,546 litre) lactation at 4 per cent butterfat, this yields 400 lb (182 kg) of butterfat. It is well to remember that if this lactation averaged 3·5 per cent butterfat, the cow would have to yield 1,120 gallons (5,091 litres) of milk, to produce the same yield of butterfat. At only 3·00 per cent butterfat, the milk yield must now rise to 1,330 gallons (6,046 litres) per 400 lb (182 kg) butterfat. This factor will become more and more important with payment for milk being increasingly based on quality.

A HEALTHY COW

The ability to resist disease is not a highly inherited character, but there is some evidence that many cow families do possess the characteristic of being prone to metabolic diseases such as staggers and milk fever. The ability to withstand disease is closely linked with longevity, and of course the older the average herd age the smaller the number of replacements needed per year.

Weakness of the legs and feet is a characteristic that is obviously inherited; evidence of the use of a bull which transmits these weaknesses are seen in far too many herds. Mastitis is known to contribute enormously to loss of milk production in the national herd, but I am sure that if the cost of lame cows and the associated loss of production and increase in numbers of cows culled were added together, this would also be a very high figure.

There is no sadder sight than to see a good old cow, or worse a good young cow, struggling to and from her grazing on sore feet. It is a trait that we should be more and more aware of, as nothing removes condition as quickly from a cow as bad feet, and of course production falls rapidly at the same time.

This condition can be controlled to some extent by carefully trimming feet, either by employing a vet or by the use of a mobile technician specialising in foot trimming, of which there are only a few as yet. Much of this foot care can be done on the farm without external help, provided great care is taken. The problem is mainly in immobilising the cow. Providing she is not too heavily in calf, by far the easiest way is to cast the cow, either in a field or on deep straw, but sadly far too few farmers are able to cast a cow properly. It should be part of the field of study of all day release and full-time courses for students of agriculture.

HERD FERTILITY

Longevity of course is not a simple characteristic, but a combination of the effects of health, fertility and management of a cow. Fertility itself is obviously highly important, and a strongly inherited characteristic. A healthy herd with good fertility, denoted by a good calving index, is extremely important towards maintaining herd profitability. The importance of calving index can be looked at, in terms of its real value, in the following way, bearing in mind the desired standard of excellence of 365 days.

100 cows with a calving index of 365 = 100 lactations and 100 calves per year.

100 cows with a calving index of 420 days = 89 lactations and 89 calves per year.

Four hundred and twenty days is not a very unusual calving index, but not only does it mean, in terms of the above example, a loss of eleven lactations and eleven calves per year, it also means that, unless the herd is calving all the year round, the seasonal calving pattern, normally autumn or spring, is put completely out of gear.

TEMPERAMENT

Anyone who has milked cows needs no convincing of the value of temperament. The unpleasantness and even danger of handling a vicious cow or heifer (being kicked and bruised by one is bad enough), but it also lengthens milking time and causes severe disruption. This in itself can cause other cows to be overmilked while the offender receives special attention.

DOGS AND STICKS?

Attention to temperament in a herd's breeding programme is vital, but unfortunately there has been little selection in the breeding of herdsmen and farmers, and it is through their reactions, and the reactions of both their dogs and their sticks (neither of which should ever come near a dairy herd), that the problem starts. A quiet, easy-to-handle herd is a sure sign of a good herdsman, and this ease of handling will be reflected very much in the herd's performance. In the parlour or cowshed, noise and disruption will be responsible often for a cow failing to let down her milk, resulting in undermilking and mastitis. All these factors are inter-related and most important.

TYPE AND CONFORMATION

There is no doubt that type, conformation and colour can be taken too far. Some points demanded by showmen, especially in the past, bore no relationship to commercial production. In defence of the breeder, with a perfect cow in his mind's eye, it will be a sad day when many of these points are not sought after, purely for their aesthetic value to please the human eye, and this is equally important whether we are considering a bovine or human female.

Type and conformation in a dairy cow is important in a modern forage-based production system. A cow needs to be reasonably large, to accommodate a large rumen, and able to deal with feed and manufacture milk. The head is not important, provided that the animal does not suffer a disability such as blindness or of overshot or undershot jaw.

If the latter condition is severe, it can prove to be a handicap to a cow's grazing ability both in the field and on the silage face, when the teeth of the bottom jaw will not meet the top jaw pad squarely and so prevent the 'tearing' action of grazing to take place. Nevertheless, other things being equal, a 'pretty' head is always better to look at than an ugly head.

LEGS AND FEET

Legs and feet are most important, as stated earlier. A straight hind leg usually means that a cow stands squarely on her hoof, and not on her heel which is soft. If a cow continually walks on her heel (the condition known as being 'heely'), this part is easily worn and damaged and her feet become sore and infected. Some cows have naturally harder feet than others, while some either develop soft feet by being reared for too long on soft muck and also from having insufficient exercise. One major advantage of housing young stock in a cubicle system as early in life as possible is that their feet are kept trim by walking on concrete.

The width of the hook and pin bones, and the length from hooks to pins, are also important. Udder attachment, both laterally and from the hind udder to the fore udder, is directly related to hook and pin bones in the majority of cows, although there are often exceptions. And of course a roomy pelvic girdle, denoted by width at the hooks, is essential for ease of calving. A cow's health can often be determined by the consistency of her coat. In general terms, a sleek smooth coat denotes good health, while some abnormalities such as a worm infestation in young cattle, or copper deficiency, can result in a rough coat, with hairs standing on end. In the Friesian breed, copper deficiency can be diagnosed in some instances by a red 'tinge' to the animal's coat.

THE PERFECT UDDER

The udder is the business end of the dairy cow, and breeding for improvement in udder conformation has been the aim of every dairy cow breeder for a very long time. I am sure that Ayrshire breeders will be delighted to read that it is the aim of every Friesian breeder to breed an Ayrshire cow udder on his cows.

A firm attachment at the rear and the front is obviously essential. Heifers with too much udder invariably 'lose' their attachment early in life. During their second or third lactation the udder becomes pendulous, prone to damage, bruising and mastitis, gets dirty very easily both summer and winter, suffers from chapped and split teats, and of course is difficult to milk. Some quartering of the udder, rather than a flat sole, is a good indication that the udder has strong suspensory ligaments and will normally last longer.

The size of teat is obviously important. This appendage has changed more dramatically than any character in a cow in the last few years. It is rare now to see large bottle teats, which are extremely

15. Good cow families are extremely important in a herd. Photograph shows three generations, from left to right: *Ullswater Sun Ray 5th,* RM, RMX, RMI, Excellent. *Ullswater Sun Ray 15th,* RM, RMX, Excellent. *Ullswater Sun Ray 27th,* RM. Ack: Mr Tom Carrick, Eden Bank, Bolton, Appleby, Westmorland.

16. An ideal dairy cow, *Ullswater Present,* RM, Excellent. Champion Royal Show 1973 and 1974. Ack: Mr Tom Carrick, Eden Bank, Bolton, Appleby, Westmorland and Mr. Ben Cooper, East Farm, Winterbourne Marketon, Swindon, Wilts.

difficult to milk. It always amazes me how a milking machine will handle a heifer's very small teats, which invariably grow to a reasonable size. Teat placings, particularly in the Friesian breed, have also improved   dramatically. This has been due to commercial pressures of larger herds demanding teats that are easily reached and fit the teat cup cluster. Ideally, teats should point downwards and not be too far apart; both front and back pairs should point slightly towards each other, especially in a heifer or young cow. The difficulty here has been of course that in its natural state, as a suckling cow, it was an advantage for the calf that its mother's teats pointed outwards. Breeders, by selection, have had to move the teats from a semi-horizontal aspect to a vertical aspect suitable for machine milking.

These points are all truly commercially important points, desirable in an efficient cow, particularly important as herds get larger and the speed and ease of milking become increasingly important.

The general look of a dairy cow is important. In general a good dairy cow gives the impression of 'dairyness' rather than of 'beefiness'. Fine boned, lean at the shoulder, fine at the withers, a fine textured skin, and not too heavy in front, deep bodied with wide hind-quarters, are all characteristics that normally point to an efficient milk-producing cow. Having noted these characters, I am very well aware of being presented many times with a most 'undairylike' cow with exceptional milking abilities.

Chapter 9

BREEDING PROGRAMMES

THE VAST CONTRIBUTION that the development of artificial insemination has made to the improvement in the dairy herd is difficult to assess in real terms. The ease with which a constructive breeding programme can be planned and, more important, the excellent service available merely by telephoning, make it very difficult to imagine how we could do without it.

Two very important aspects of the benefits of an artificial insemination service stand out above all the others as contributions to herd improvement. The first is the availability of good progeny-tested bulls, and the second, the ability to progeny-test young bulls relatively quickly and efficiently, and with a fair degree of accuracy to maintain and improve the standard of bulls available for service.

Many successful young bulls used for artificial insemination have started their working lives in a single or group of herds being used for natural service. This source of bulls is very important and it is hoped that it will continue. Depending on the number of daughters available, a very good preliminary assessment of the bull's breeding value can be obtained, particularly in terms of his daughters' commercially important characters—udder shape and size, teat shape, size and placement, legs, feet and temperament and overall size of the animals. It is, however, very difficult to assess the bull's daughters' true production characters, with the relatively small number of daughters that are available, but even so, such an assessment can be a very good guide to the bull's value when used later on a much wider scale through artificial insemination.

One of the difficulties with this system of testing is that the bull is at least six and more often over eight years of age before he has been assessed, even when used on a large farm. The intervening period has meant that this bull has been used extensively while still unproven, or has been laid off on the farm, which in terms of feed alone is an expensive business.

Whoever coined the term 'contemporary comparison' was particularly successful in choosing a phrase that goes a long way towards being self-explanatory. It simply means a comparison of any

95

single bull's daughters with that of his herd mates or contemporaries sired by other bulls in that herd or herds. We see immediately why numbers, and their spread over many herds, are important, in that the greater the numbers involved and the greater the variation of the conditions that they are subject to in many herds, the more reliance can be put on the comparison.

As a very simple, but very common, example, let us compare two unproven bulls A and B which are working in natural service. Twenty heifers per year enter the herd and we will assume for convenience that they are evenly distributed, ten being by each bull. Each year, therefore, only ten first lactations are available to test with their contemporaries, which is far too low a number to give an account and assessment of the bull's worth. Assume that the ten daughters from Bull A average 900 gallons (4,091 litres) in 305 days in their first lactation, while under identical conditions Bull B's daughters average 1,000 gallons (4,546 litres) in 305 days. Bull B has, on these figures, a superiority of exactly 100 gallons (455 litres) over Bull A. Bull B is certainly the superior bull when we consider these figures; the problem lies, however, in trying to answer the question, 'Were both these bulls inferior or superior to the national average?' If this was a herd, heavily fed, with heifers calving at two years nine months, and normally expected to give 1,100 gallons (5,000 litres) in their first lactation, both bulls may therefore be inferior and both result in reduced milk yields, A by 200 gallons (909 litres) per year, and B by 100 gallons (455 litres).

Testing these bulls through the medium of artificial insemination on a large scale can go a long way towards eliminating these doubts. Bulls with daughters milking in 40, 50 or even larger herds will be performing side by side with their contemporaries sired by a very large number of bulls. The contemporary daughters together will form a sample far nearer the 'average' heifers from which meaningful and fairly acceptable comparisons can be made.

Selection of many young bulls for use in artificial insemination by the Milk Marketing Board follows a very well planned procedure. In the first instance, potential bull mothers are sought and examined for their superiority in producing quantity and quality of milk. This means that a cow that consistently, as a mature cow, gives 1,800 gallons (8,182 litres), while her herd mates give 1,200 gallons (5,455 litres), is clearly a superior cow. These cows are usually chosen after they have milked at least four lactations, and other important commercial characters are taken into account—udder, teats, legs, feet, temperament, size and 'wearability'. If she satisfies all these fairly stringent criteria, she is then chosen as a 'contract-mating cow' and is then mated to one of the most successful progeny-tested bulls standing at an artificial insemination centre. Bull calves from these matings (heifer calves obviously remain as a bonus to the breeder) are bought by the Board after visual inspection for physical defects. They are then reared at the Board's Chippenham bull-rearing centre.

An added bonus of central rearing is that the growth characteristics of these bulls can also be noted. In fact it is a performance test. With the Friesian breed in particular this is important, as a very large proportion of that bull's male calves will be reared for beef eventually. At about ten months of age, if they are producing sufficient semen, which must of course be also of good quality, they are used at random for some 500 matings in milk-recorded herds.

As many of these matings as possible are planned under the Dairy Progeny Testing Scheme (DPTS). This scheme relies on dairy farmers who are willing to use young unproven bulls on their herds, with the added incentive of reduced fees. To these farmers the scheme is to some extent a gamble, although only a relatively small proportion of the herd can be contracted in this way. They may be lucky and have daughters produced by sires who will later become top bulls; conversely many of these bulls will turn out to be no better, and some worse, than average. The chances are fairly high that no one bull will produce disastrous results in any one herd, as of course only a few female progeny will be sired by any one untested bull in a herd.

Every dairy farmer should be grateful and acknowledge the service that participants of DPTS or similar schemes by commercial companies are giving. In the same way commercial milk producers should acknowledge the fact that a fair proportion of producers must record milk quantity and quality through National Milk Records. Without them it would be impossible to assess bulls suitable for use on successive generations of cows. It is very easy to opt out of such schemes and rely on 'the others' to produce the data needed to maintain and improve the efficiency of our national herd.

RESULT OF 500 MATINGS BY ONE BULL

It is worth looking at the predicted numbers of milk recorded daughters that will be sired by any one bull as a result of 500 matings, and startling how only information of about 100–120 daughter lactations are produced.

From this simple calculation, which takes a realistic look at losses, transfers, etc, only 100 to 120 heifers will form the progeny testing groups, and even this is possibly an optimistic figure. MMB figures suggest that on average only about 60–80 recorded daughters remain in the herd of birth, to complete their first lactation. We see therefore that 500 services is the very minimum that can be used for testing, to give a realistic and reasonably accurate progeny test result.

500 services	70% conception	350 pregnancies
350 pregnancies	6% losses at birth	330 live births
330 live births	50% bull calves	165 heifer calves
165 heifer calves	8% rearing losses	140 heifers
140 heifers	1% loss at rearing	138 bulling heifers
138 bulling heifers	Sales, infertility, deaths, accidents, losses at calving, summer mastitis—10%	124 milking heifers
124 milking heifers	Sales, accidents etc during first lactation—5%	118 recorded first lactations

Many commercial breeding organisations and syndicates also employ similar programmes to test young bulls. Use of all young bulls for progeny testing is strictly controlled by the Ministry of Agriculture who grant all licences for the sale and use of semen. In some instances these rules are too stringent, especially when a young bull has proved to be of exceptional merit when used in one herd but has insufficient daughters for general use. Very often these bulls are seven years of age before they are spotted, and a further progeny test through AI will mean that they will be far too old when this is completed to make an impact on the national herd. In many instances, however, these stringent conditions prevent 'salesmanship' overtaking results and does not allow unproven, and often inferior, bulls being used. It also prevents the spread of congenital disorders, such as bulldog calves, on a large scale.

I have discussed the meaning of contemporary comparison in its wider sense. Actual calculation will vary, and will no doubt change with time, but the most recent change is the use of a very unfortunate term, 'Improved Contemporary Comparisons', which gives, at first sight, the impression that it refers to the fact that a bull's breeding value has recently improved.

The reason for this change is that the old contemporary comparison did not take into account important factors such as seasonality of calving, autumn calvers being known to yield, on average, more than their herd mates calving in spring or summer. Age of calving effect is of course removed and corrected for. With this improvement the improved contemporary comparison has become more accurate and meaningful in assessing a bull's breeding worth. This was also necessary as due to the continued use of 'good' bulls in the national herd, it was becoming more and more difficult for a young bull to compare with other proven bulls, and a +60-gallon

(273 litres) bull in 1960 may well have been a +20-gallon (+91 litre) bull in 1974. This genetic improvement has now been calculated and allowed for, with a consequent better chance for a current young bull to prove his true worth.

'BULL OF THE DAY'

The majority of herds still rely on the use of the 'bull of the day', taking for granted that bulls available at stud in their area are well bred and that the majority of them will have above average milk production characteristics. This is perfectly acceptable and also it is the cheapest method of using the AI services. The trend is increasing, however, towards the use of the more expensive (in terms of initial cost) nominated service: the selection of bulls, often with the help of a field officer, that are most likely to do most good in herds. This selection may be designed to improve milk yield in a low-producing herd and improve butterfat in a herd known to be consistently low in fat, by using bulls to correct leg weaknesses, increase size, etc, or by attempting to correct, by the use of the right bull, any other faults. No bull will correct all faults, and the more factors that are selected for, the more difficult it is to obtain the desired result. With heifers, a bull may well be selected to give easier calving, a very important point as we move nearer to two year old calving in many herds.

NOMINATED SIRES

This nominated service demands an extra charge, depending on the excellence of the bull and the related demand for his semen. In many instances, this extra charge is a very worthwhile investment, in that the resultant progeny helps to improve the herd. Some bulls inevitably become very popular, and a waiting list is formed. It is gratifying, however, for the producer who participates in the Dairy Progeny Testing Scheme of the Milk Marketing Board that he will have some preferential treatment if he nominates popular bulls, as a just reward for his willingness to participate in the testing schemes.

Milk producing herds rely on maintaining or increasing their efficiency, and there is no doubt that the use of good bulls, through artificial insemination, has benefited and increased this efficiency enormously. Using a bull with a contemporary comparison of only a modest +20 gallons (+91 litres) will give, at today's prices (1975), an extra £26 of milk over an average productive life of four lactations. In real terms the same cow may well milk for five lactations, rather than the average four, and the real worth now, in terms of extra milk, and more important still, decrease in replacement cost, will be far greater.

COSTS AND RETURNS OF USING GOOD BULLS

If this insemination costs £3 extra per cow, and if one heifer enters the herd as a result of every three inseminations, the extra cost per heifer is £3 × 3 = £9. The return is therefore at least £26 for an investment of £9. The use of a +100-gallon (+454 litres) bull similarly will mean, by the same calculation, £130-worth of extra milk, and possibly £5 per service. Now we have the situation of £130 extra return for an investment of £15, which is very good business. We can continue this train of thought much further of course, assuming that these higher producing progeny are more efficient converters of feed into milk, and as a result we get the extra milk with no increase, or very little increase in inputs.

If a herd had been continually built up on the use of +100-gallon (+454 litre) bulls to the point when all cows were of this potential on average, the results in extra milk sales in a 100-cow herd per annum is a staggering figure in excess of £3,000. Even allowing for some possible extra inputs of concentrates, this is a sum that can contribute handsomely to herd profitability.

SELECTING SIRES FOR INDIVIDUAL CIRCUMSTANCES

In future there is no doubt that we will be able to choose bulls that produce daughters that will be more efficient producers under individual systems. In our herd at Frondeg there are cows that are obviously more suited to producing milk from a mainly grass and silage diet than others. With an average 1,000 gallons (4,546 litres) per year sold, yields vary from 750 gallons (3,409 litres) to 1,600 gallons (7,273 litres) under identical conditions. We would like to identify bulls that will produce cows that, when mature, will produce in excess of 1,200 gallons (5,455 litres) under our system. One word ot warning. I am very dubious of the potential of Canadian Holstein-type cows under this type of system. Selection in Canada and in the United States has been based on systems that rely on high energy, good quality diets based on maize, maize silage and lucerne hay. Under our system, especially with high stocking rates, the factor that is against this type of cow is her very high maintenance requirements.

USE OF BEEF BULLS

In any herd there are good cows from which it is desirable to rear their progeny for herd replacement; equally there are cows—low yielders, cows with poor feet or bad temperament, low quality milk—from whom it is obviously not desirable to breed. The average length of time that an individual cow remains in the herd in the United Kingdom is about four lactations. This means that some 25 new heifers have to be brought into a 100-cow herd every year. If this herd life could be extended to five years, this has the effect of decreasing the requirement for heifers to 20 per year, which substantially reduces the replacement cost. The increase in the proportion of adult cows in the herd also results in a higher proportion of mature cow yields, compared with the usually lower heifer yields, with a consequent increase in the volume of milk sold per annum in the herd.

Ideally, it is desirable to bull the poorer cows in the herd with a beef bull for two reasons. There is then no temptation to rear heifer calves from these inferior cows, and of course beef-cross calves demand a premium when sold for beef, increasing herd profitability. The proportion of cows available for beef-crossing will vary with the replacement rate as is shown in Table 1.

Table 1. Effect of Three Levels of Culling on Selection of Cows for Breeding in Three 100-cow Friesian Herds.

	Herd A	Herd B	Herd C
No of replacements per annum	20	25	30
No of heifer calves needed per year allowing for losses and infertility, etc	23	28	33
Total no of mature cows available	80	75	70
No of cows to Friesian bull	46	56	66
No of poorest cows to beef bull	34	19	4
	High rate of dam selection	Medium rate of dam selection	Virtually no selection of dams

The importance of longevity in a herd is very clearly shown here, if there is to be any degree of selection of cows as replacement mothers. It is interesting that a herd of 100 cows needing 30 heifers per year is barely self sufficient, and often is not, if other management practices fall below average, such as high calf mortality or a high rate of cow infertility.

Chapter 10

MILKING THE DAIRY HERD

I AM ALWAYS amused to see a farmer spending many thousands of pounds on a combine harvester, which is used at most for six weeks of the year to harvest 120 acres (48·5 hectares) of cereals, plus a few more thousand pounds on drying and storage equipment, and yet he is often most reluctant to spend the same amount, or often considerably less, on a milking parlour to milk 120 cows, twice a day for 365 days of the year.

It is essential to provide the best milking facilities that the business can afford. Whether the owner does the milking himself, or employs other men to do it, working under difficult conditions may be tolerated for a few days, or even weeks, but it is having to put up with unsatisfactory conditions day after day for a long period that produces problems. It is when the herdsman is off colour that difficult conditions cause slip-ups. This is followed by less attention to detail (the odd cow is under- or over-milked), a loss of temper, a raised voice, even a degree of violence. These little points, taken collectively, are almost sure to result in less efficiency and the attention to detail that is absolutely essential to obtain the best results from the herd.

The herringbone parlour forms the basic standard of milking set-ups in United Kingdom.

Nevertheless there are a very large number of tandem parlours, a few chutes, and a surprisingly high number of abreast and bail milkers. The rotary parlour, new in 1969 to this country, has also increased in numerical strength and can be described probably as the Rolls Royce of current equipment, but, as we well know, few of us can afford to run a Rolls.

DEVELOPMENT OF THE MOVABLE BAIL

The abreast parlour is in fact a fixed edition of the bail, pioneered on the Wiltshire Downs by Hosier in the 1920's. The bail was developed to allow cows to be milked out on the Downs, away from the homestead. In summer, the herd was milked where the grass grew, only returning to the steading in winter where the cows were loose-housed in straw yards, and the mobile bail came with the cows. A few

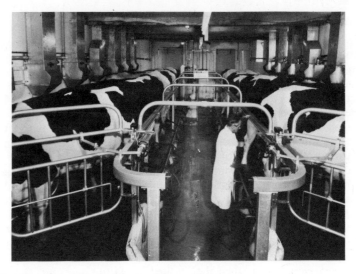

17. 16 unit/16 stall herringbone parlour with low level jars.

are still in action, but to milk in them on a cold frosty January morning is, to say the least, an unpleasant experience both for cows and men. Clusters are frozen, air lines full of ice deposits, and milk lines blocked by frozen water.

THE ABREAST-TYPE PARLOUR

With the move from byre-housing to loose-housing, the abreast parlour became very popular, largely because it was the only type available. There were immediate advantages compared with using the bucket plant. The development of in-churn milking units saved very considerable effort and time in carrying milk in buckets. Another advantage of course was that it was far easier to maintain a clean, relatively small six- or eight-stall parlour, rather than a 40- to 50-stall cowshed both in winter and summer.

In-churn milking soon gave way to pipeline milking, firstly to a distribution point where, before or after cooling, the milk could be equally distributed by a simple device, to fill four or six churns in the dairy simultaneously. Later of course the development of the refrigerated bulk milk tank removed the chore of churn watching and the constant fear of milk spillage.

BYRE MILKING

It is often forgotten that a very large number of cows are still housed in byres, tied by the neck, and milked in the byre. The task of carrying milk to the dairy, or central receiving point in the large byre, is difficult and laborious. The installation of a pipeline milking system has eliminated this chore and undoubtedly has been responsible for cleaner milk production, as open buckets, full or empty, are never exposed to the byre atmosphere. The installation of a bulk tank often results in this system being remarkably efficient, as only the milk cluster and lines have to be moved from cow to cow; there is no letting-in time or letting-out time during milking, nor any waiting time while the glass jar of a parlour is emptied. However, an extra burden (especially in summer) is of course the tying up of cows and letting them loose after milking. To see a 100 or more excellent cows tied up and awaiting milking is a sight well worth seeing, particularly if it is an Ayrshire herd with beautiful udders. This sight at David Howie's Morwick herd, in Acklington, Northumberland, impressed our students very much when they visited his farm.

DEVELOPMENT OF HERRINGBONE PARLOURS

The development of the herringbone parlour was a great step forward in speeding up and improving milking efficiency, even though many owners of high yielding herds will still say that individual cow attention is lost, particularly at milking. We must balance this with the fact that labour is expensive, and herds, to combat decreasing profits, have expanded, so that one man has to milk 100 cows, or even more, on his own.

The herringbone parlour allows one man to milk this number of cows very efficiently without having to work at great speed. Because the cows are closely grouped he has not got to walk vast distances during milking, there is no handling of milk and, more important still, the length of time spent milking is limited and therefore reduces fatigue. With six units a good man can manage 50 to 60 cows per man hour, while 35 cows per hour with an abreast parlour is a reasonable standard. These figures are of course dependent on the man and the stage of lactation of the cows.

Herringbone parlours are, however, not without their problems. If meal or cubes are to be fed in the parlour, the feeding system has to be fairly elaborate, employing levers and vacuum- or electrically-controlled rationing machines, as there is no access to the cow's manger, as in a tandem or even an abreast parlour, unless one has a feeding passage. This in most situations is impractical, as it means that the operator, and more often than not there is only one, has to leave the pit during milking. Slow milkers and high yielders, or even slow feeders, can slow down the whole process as turnout of a group is governed by the slowest milker, while in an abreast or tandem parlour only the offending cow (if she is a slow milker) or most useful cow (if she is a high yielder) needs to stay in her stall until the milking is completed, and this in no way upsets the routine.

THE TANDEM PARLOUR

Half way between the abreast and the herringbone is the tandem parlour. It has its advantages, again in that a cow can remain in her stall for as long as required without upsetting the routine, or if individual attention is needed. Tandems tend to be relatively slow throughput installations, and the distance walked during milking is again large. The greatest drawback is that the operator is continually opening and closing gates, which is in fact the cause of the slow throughput. Thirty to thirty-five cows with a six-stall three-unit is the maximum rate for this type of parlour, with a few cows per hour extra for a six-stall six-unit parlour.

Up to 1969 the choice of milking parlours was either an abreast, tandem, chute or herringbone. The choice depended on the size of the herd obviously, and with up to 50 cows the abreast is still as good a parlour as any, particularly if high yields per cow are the aim as it allows for individual attention, plus reasonable throughput, and is reasonably priced.

Somewhere in the middle came the tandem, but I have never been very impressed with its performance. Again attention to individuals is possible for maximum yields based on high cake feeding, but it never became very popular.

THE POSITION OF MILK LINES

The herringbone of course caught on dramatically, and there are very many variations to this type of parlour, mostly involving shape of rump rail, arrangements for feeding, and in particular level of the milk jar. The position of these jars has been going up and down like yo-yos over the past few years, but seems to have finally settled either about 6' (1·8 m) above floor level or below cow level, with a tendency (becoming popular) at about udder level.

The advantages claimed for having the jars, or in many new installations a milk line only, below cow level is that this reduces fluctuations in vacuum levels, and that milking is faster.

A low line herringbone installation demands doubling up of cluster numbers to one per stall, and its advantage must be speeding up milking time per cow, but it is doubtful whether this actually speeds up throughput per hour, as this is controlled to a large extent by cow movements, etc in and out of the parlour.

There are of course many disadvantages of a low line milker. The cleaning of glass and rubber is far more difficult, accessibility is more difficult, and recording by visual examination of jar levels far more difficult than with a high line system.

TWO STALLS OR ONE STALL PER UNIT?

Ideally, any milking parlour should be a one-man unit. Two or more men in a parlour pit has very often the same effect as putting two good cooks in a small kitchen, and for many herds the ideal is a five- or six-a-side herringbone parlour with one man. Most of these parlours have been designed as twelve-stall, six-unit, with the units swinging alternatively from side to side.

When conditions are ideal and cows are behaving well, this swing-over system works like clockwork. Cows ènter on one side, are washed, fed and just at the time when milk let-down is complete, the cows are ready on the other side, and the clusters are then swung over to them. This is often the ideal situation for the first few fillings of the parlour, when incidentally most of the well behaved cows usually come in, and the first 40 cows can normally be milked at a very rapid rate. It is the next 40 with the usual normal complement of irritable cows, chapped teats, jumpy heifers and slow milkers that cause the troubles, and immediately the smooth pattern goes wrong. With this swing-over system it becomes almost a crime to hang up a cluster, as the whole system is designed for their constant use, and with hanging up, the milker starts to think that he is being inefficient.

The doubled-up plant is more expensive—a 12-stall herringbone has 12 units—but the system has its advantages. It is *designed* so that clusters can be hung up during part of the routine, and this relieves the tension, provided of course that the operator does not resort to overmilking. Doubling up does not dramatically increase throughput in terms of cows per hour, but is essential for a low line set-up, and desirable where an automatic cluster removal system is installed.

THE LATEST—THE ROTARY PARLOUR

Progress in agricultural technology is being made continually and just as we thought that our milking technology had reached its peak with herringbone parlours, a brand new concept—the rotary parlour—was developed on a commercial scale, although there have been a few operating throughout the world for some time. The concept has now changed dramatically, in that with all other parlours

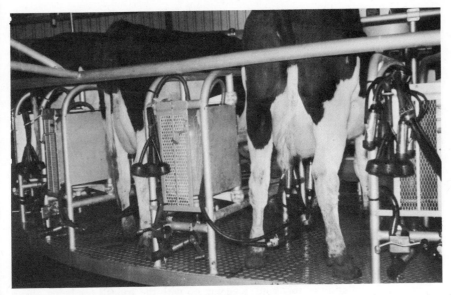

18. Cows being milked in a rotary abreast, or turnstile, parlour.

19. 14 unit rotary herringbone parlour.

we rely on the cow standing still, while the operator moves. With the rotary the cow is moved mechanically on a raised platform in a complete circle, with either the operator within, or outside, this circle.

A fairly substantial sum of money is needed to install one of these parlours, and the very minimum number of cows that will warrant this high capital cost is one hundred. Like any other new technical development it is of no use jumping on the bandwagon (or rotary parlour) until the farmer asks himself some very pertinent questions:

(1) Is the cost justified; do I save a commensurate sum of money in labour?
(2) Do I make working conditions so much better for the man handling the system?
(3) Will this allow me to keep more cows?
(4) Will better conditions increase milk yield or cut down feed costs?

It is only after all (or most of) the answers to these questions have been satisfactorily answered that the owner should contemplate an installation of this kind. Keeping up with the Jones's (or being ahead of them) can give some people considerable satisfaction but for many, a far cheaper installation will have to be seriously considered.

With a large herd of cows, there is no doubt that a rotary parlour can be justified. Good operators are scarce and command high wages, but if their expertise can be spread over a large number of cows, this is good business.

There is also one other very important point. There is a limit to the time that any one operator can concentrate sufficiently to milk cows efficiently, as milking demands mental concentration and energy. This is roughly some two to two-and-a-half hours in the morning and about two hours in the afternoon. This time will of course vary, especially with the temperament of the man or woman milking. A good reply that I once had to the question, "How long can a man or woman milk?" was, "Until he or she starts counting how many cows are left in the collecting yard". We have all had this experience, the first 100 pass through and breakfast seems only a few minutes away. The last 20 cows seem to take ages, and hunger becomes more and more acute, and inevitably the quality of your work suffers.

There are three basic types of rotary parlours. The *rotary tandem*, normally has between 6 and 14 stalls, with outputs of between 60 cows an hour with one man, to 80 cows per hour with two men. The fatiguing and time-consuming job of opening and shutting gates of the fixed tandem is overcome by automation, and increases efficiency. The distance to be walked, especially in a one-man unit, is quite large.

However, a cow that is slow to milk, or a high yielder, can be sent round a second time with this type of parlour without upsetting the routine at all.

The *rotary herringbone* has the advantage of a fixed herringbone, in that distances walked are reduced as the centre circle is relatively much smaller, compared with a tandem with an equal number of stalls.

ROTARY PARLOURS—RATES OF WORK

Sizes of rotary herringbone parlours vary from 12-point to 28-point models. Throughputs per man will be discussed later, but I give below manufacturers' claims for throughputs:

12-point	85– 90 cows per hour	(one man)
14-point	90– 95 cows per hour	(one man)
18-point	140–150 cows per hour	(two men)
28-point	200–240 cows per hour	(two or three men)

The latest, and a design that could possibly become more popular than other rotaries, is the *rotary abreast,* also known as the 'Turnstile' type. Cows in this parlour face the centre of the circle, with operators (and normally this demands two operators) on the outside of the circle. Sizes and claimed throughputs are:

20-point	150–160 cows per hour	(two men)
23-point	190–200 cows per hour	(two men)
30-point	200–240 cows per hour	(three men)

Two men are normally required for this system. If only one man is milking, the cows are out of view of the operator for a considerable period of time. Often one man washes cows, feeds and puts on clusters, while the second man replaces fallen clusters and removes them at the end of milk flow. Cows back out of the system normally on completion of the round, but one excellent system I saw in New Zealand was built on the side of a steep hill and had a central exit passage through which cows left the parlour and emerged down below through a tunnel. This design is impossible in many areas, but may make many a steep hill on a Welsh dairy farm valuable!

AUTOMATIC CLUSTER REMOVAL

Automatic cluster removers are progressively becoming more sophisticated and reliable. They depend on sensors which detect the decline in flow of milk and, either mechanically or by vacuum, cut off the vacuum supply to the teat cups and remove them. Some more recent designs also have a built-in system whereby pressure, similar to the action of manual machine stripping, is exerted on the clusters for a few seconds at the end of milk flow. These can be fitted to any parlour, but herringbone and rotary parlours are particularly suited to an automatic cluster removal system. Many will argue that this is bringing the skills of milking into the realms of factory automation, but as these systems are improved, there is no doubt that they will prevent over milking and its associated dangers, particularly the spread of mastitis infection. Consequently, this will ease the work load of the operators and speed up milking.

MILKING PARLOUR THROUGHPUTS

Earlier in this chapter I have discussed manufacturers' claims for parlour throughputs with various types of milking installations. The attaining of their standards are of course dependent on the efficiency, inherent ability and of the skills of the operators. Unfortunately many surveys have shown that a very large proportion of herdsmen do not achieve these rates.

The milking process can be divided into a number of routine jobs for the operator. These are shown in Table 2, together with the time tables per cow as given by Barnard, Halley and Scott* for two types of parlour, the abreast and herringbone, each with two stalls per unit.

Table 2. Basic Elements of Work Routine in Abreast and Herringbone Parlour without Milk Recording or Meal Feeding.*

Element description	Abreast	Herringbone
	Two stalls per unit (seconds)	
Wash cow	25	20
Use strip cup	9	5
Move to adjacent cow	2	1
Machine strip	24	15
Remove cluster and transfer	4	3
Apply cluster to prepared cow	7	7
Move to adjacent or opposite point	2	1
Batch changeover (6 cows)	—	5
Cow transfer	9	—
Fasten retaining chain	4	—
Move to next work point	3	1
Average work routine time (at standard performance)	89	58
Add about 15% for contingencies (slow milkers, uneasy cows etc)	14	9
TOTAL	103	67

*Barnard, C. S., Halley, R. J. and Scott, A. H. 'Milk Production' Iliffe Books Ltd, London 1970.

In simple terms, to milk sixty cows per hour, in any parlour the operator must carry out the relevant routine in one minute. This routine time is extremely important in determining the maximum number of cows that one man can handle.

Table 2 gives a work routine when a single operator is working fairly quickly and efficiently. Therefore with a 2:1 abreast parlour, each cow takes up 103 seconds to perform the routine associated with her and therefore the maximum number of cows that one man can handle in an hour with his routine in any abreast parlour is simply 3,600 seconds ÷ 103 seconds = 35 cows per hour. Similarly, with a herringbone, using the above figures, throughput in a herringbone can be measured thus:

$$3600 \div 67 = 54 \text{ cows per hour.}$$

Having calculated the maximum cows that one man can handle in a parlour, this does not give the number of units that one man can handle. This will be dependent on another factor, the time actually spent with clusters on, when the cow is actually milking. With the examples given in Table 2, the man may be capable of milking 54 cows per hour, provided of course the actual time with 'machines on' is not limiting. As an extreme example, consider attempting to milk 54 cows per hour with one man in a two-stall, one-unit herringbone parlour. This means that as 54 cows pass through the parlour every hour, with one unit the maximum time spent actually milking can only be 67 seconds, which is clearly impossible.

At this point we have to consider the average time spent actually milking in relation to yield. The careful use of the word 'average' is important here, as speed of milking varies appreciably from cow to cow, from very rapid to, unfortunately, extremely slow.

EFFECT OF YIELD PER COW

Table 3 published in Eire by An Foras Taluntais* gives the relationship between yield per milking and the time when the machine is actually on the cow. These figures will vary, especially with all-the-year-round calvers, but the important fact is that differences between cows will be evened out somewhat, so that we end with average figures as given on page 112.

To return to the example of a herringbone parlour with a maximum throughput, governed by the man's time taken in routine jobs other than milking. If a herd is averaging 30 lb (13·60 kg) per milking, it needs 6·83 minutes or 410 seconds milking time according to Table 3. Routine time (from Table 2) for a herringbone two-stall one-unit parlour is 67 seconds. Therefore, to allow sufficient time for milking

*An Foras Taluntais. Milking equipment and installations, 1972.

and routine preparation, etc, these two figures must be considered together. By dividing one figure by the other we obtain the number of units that one man can handle, that is, the number of cows an operator can prepare during milk flow time of a line of cows.

Table 3. Relationship between Milk Yield and Milk-flow Time *

| Milk yield per milking | | Milk-flow time (minutes) |
lb	kg	
10	(4·53)	3·57
20	(9·07)	5·20
30	(13·60)	6·83
40	(18·14)	8·46

* Barnard, C. S., Halley, R. J. and Scott, A. H. 'Milk Production' Illiffe Books Ltd, London. 1970.

Thus with our example $\dfrac{410}{67}$ $\dfrac{\text{milking time per cow}}{\text{seconds routine}}$ $= 6$ units/man.
time per cow

Let us look at this calculation from another angle. Each cow yielding in this case 30 lb (6·85 kg) on one side of the milking parlour, on average takes 410 seconds actual milking time. During this time the operator has time to deal with the routine work associated with each of the other milking units in the parlour as described in Table 2, including letting cows in and out in batches. The operator can therefore perform this routine taking 67 seconds per cow, six times during the time that one side is being milked. He can therefore comfortably manage six units without undue overmilking, but perhaps to allow a safety margin, five units would be more appropriate.

It is very interesting to remember that the higher the average yield per cow in a parlour, the more time the operator has to perform the routine jobs. Conversely, the lower the yield (at drying-off time, for example), the harder he has to work to prevent overmilking as the following examples (given in Table 4) will show, with times again taken from Tables 2 and 3 with a two-stall one-unit herringbone.

Table 4. Relationship between Yield per Milking and Time Available to Perform Routine Work in a 12-stall 6-unit Herringbone Parlour. *

Herd	Yield per milking	Actual milking time	Time available per cow for routine
A	20 lb (9·07 kg)	5·20 min (312 secs)	$\dfrac{312}{6} = 52$ seconds
B	30 lb (13·60 kg)	6·83 min (410 secs)	$\dfrac{410}{6} = 68$ seconds
C	40 lb (18·14 kg)	8·46 min (508 secs)	$\dfrac{508}{6} = 85$ seconds

* Barnard, C. S., Halley, R. J. and Scott, A. H. 'Milk Production' Illiffe Books Ltd, London. 1970.

MILK YIELD PER HOUR

From Tables 2, 3 and 4, and using the routine described, we see that Herd A (Table 4) operator will be hard pushed to achieve maximum output, as routine time (67 seconds) is greater than time available and his output per hour, at approximately 54 cows per hour, will be governed by routine work rather than yield per cow. Operator with Herd B will, however, find that time available matches perfectly with time needed for routine tasks, at approximately 54 cows per hour. But with Herd C the operator will find that he has plenty of time for routine work and thus the throughput of this herd is now controlled by the average milk yield of the herd. The maximum number of cows that can be milked is now 3,600 seconds ÷ 85 seconds = 42 cows per hour.

When comparing milk produced per hour, we see below the differences between the three herds.

Table 5. Relationship between Yield per Cow, Throughput of Cows per Hour, and Milk Produced per Hour in a 12-stall 6-unit Herringbone Parlour. *

	Milk yields per milking	Cows per hour	Milk yield per hour
Herd A	20 lb (9·07 kg)	54	108 gallons (490 litres)
Herd B	30 lb (13·60 kg)	54	162 gallons (736 litres)
Herd C	40 lb (18·14 kg)	42	168 gallons (763 litres)

* Barnard, C. S., Halley, R. J. and Scott, A. H. 'Milk Production' Illiffe Books Ltd, London. 1970.

Each installation required similar calculations to the above to determine type of parlour, number of units, etc in relation to herd size, milk yields and so on. Looking at figures in Table 3 one has to wonder how a rotary abreast parlour with 28 stalls can ever handle 240 cows per hour. This is a particularly good example to consider as it shows how to answer a very important question that is often asked, "How can I milk 240, or any other number of cows, per hour?" I have already shown in Table 2, that with a herringbone parlour it takes a minimum of 67 seconds per cow if only one man is available. One answer to the question of increased throughput is of course putting two men in the parlour and increasing the number of units. It is often doubtful whether putting two men in a parlour doubles throughput, but it can achieve very near this if, for example, by doubling the size of a herringbone from a 12-stall, 6-unit, to a 24-stall, 12-unit installation, with corresponding potential being raised from 50 to near 90 or 100 cows per hour.

Another way of increasing throughput is to drop some of the routine jobs, but this is not to be recommended. For example, discontinuing udder washing (20 seconds), use of strip cup (5 seconds) and machine stripping (15 seconds) would reduce routine by 40 seconds per cow in a herringbone parlour. (This could be further reduced by installing automatic cluster removers). In the same manner the work routine in a herringbone would be reduced to below 30 seconds per cow, and while not recommended, it is possible to speed up milking by allowing one man to handle more units. Discontinuing washing and use of strip cup, apart from their obvious disadvantages will increase actual milking time, in that no stimulus will have been given to the udder prior to milking; milk let-down will thus not coincide with, but will be later than, actually putting on the teat cups.

HIGH THROUGHPUT PARLOURS—HOW MANY MEN?

With 240 cows per hour milked in a rotary abreast parlour, the time for routine work, if only one man is available, is 15 seconds, which is clearly bordering the impossible. Simpler calculations we can make therefore are:

If 30 seconds per cow for routine is needed—2 operators
If 45 seconds per cow for routine is needed—3 operators

Ease of feeding, with one point only or computer-controlled feeding, the relative ease of washing and putting on clusters by one man without moving from a single point, and possibly automatic cluster removal, reduces routine time needed. In this situation, however, two operators at least are needed, and more normally three—one for washing udders and putting on clusters, and the second generally attending to fallen-off clusters, cow entry, collecting yard fill, etc, and a third machine stripping, removing clusters and watching cow exits from the parlour.

CHOOSING A MILKING PARLOUR

The examples I have given serve as an introduction only to the various considerations and calculations necessary in choosing a parlour. Probably the most popular design for some years yet will be the 5/10 herringbone. Why not the 6/12? The answer to this question is very important. Calculations already done clearly show that one man can handle a 6/12 parlour quite satisfactorily, but would he have those extra few seconds available to note the yield of the cow, and from this deduce that she is down appreciably in milk? Is she bulling or off colour? Is the cow off her food for a possible variety of reasons?

Would he detect a few clots in the milk this evening, rather than a large swollen quarter with mastitis the following morning? Does the system allow him to observe the odd lame cow or uneasy cows in the parlour, warning him of possible sub-clinical staggers in spring, and thereby giving him ample time to feed more magnesium-rich concentrates to counteract this.

These factors do not enter into calculations of 'short-term efficiency' but may be of enormous importance in the long-term efficiency of the herd, maintaining milk yield, herd health, a good calving index and so on—all those points that distinguish a milker from a herdsman.

UDDER WASHING

There is no faster and more affective way of spreading mastitis than by the use of udder cloths, unless extreme care is taken with their use, and a suitable sterilising agent used during washing and for their storage between milking.

This routine task has been greatly improved by the development of a simple sprinkler udder-washing system, with long flexible tubes hanging from above the parlour, where a thermostatically controlled heater tank is placed. By pressing a valve, or simple tap, a clean sprinkle of blood heat water is available, often containing a sterilising agent incorporated by syphoning.

The use of disposable paper towels, one for each cow, has also eased the problem of mastitis spread, although this is still possible by hand contamination. The use of blood heat water, rather than often cold water from a bucket, has the effect of causing more rapid let-down of milk and results in quieter cows. In fact using warm water is often far less dangerous for the operator, especially when you see the reaction of a nervous cow on a frosty morning when a cold udder-washing cloth is slapped on to her udder.

FEEDING IN THE PARLOUR

A Frenchman, with a very successful large dairy unit, told me a few very interesting facts about feeding in the parlour. I was remarking, whilst in his scrupulously clean 12-point rotary tandem parlour, that there were no feeding arrangements in the stalls. He asked me whether I had ever seen a cow dunging when suckling a calf. On reflection I had to answer that I had not. He added that a cow often dunged when eating from a trough. He also asked whether a cow would normally stop grazing when suckling a calf, which is again perfectly true.

The conclusion that he had come to is quite easily and logically followed from the above discussion. Cows should not be offered food when milking, and this made the chances of dunging in the parlour minimal. I know that our parlour in summer, when the cows are not being fed there, is cleaner than in the early spring when they are being fed concentrates.

WHY FEED IN THE PARLOUR?

The milking parlour is a very convenient point to feed concentrates to the herd, that is, if concentrate feeding is desirable at all. In most herds it is the only time that cows can be given individual attention, and although a basic ration can be given to a herd behind a feed barrier or trough set-up, the cows can only be group-fed by this arrangement. The herd cannot be fed in relation to individual cow performance and requirements, and often big, fast-eating cows fare far better than timid, young cows or heifers.

Photo 11 (page 73) shows the fairly simple arrangement at Frondeg, where a high proportion of the herd's concentrate ration is fed. As an example, we will consider at six-week calved cow giving seven gallons (31·8 litres) of milk a day in February, eating sufficient silage of good quality to give Maintenance + one gallon (M +1) (M + 4·5 litres) in terms of energy requirement, and M +3 gallons (M + 13·6 litres) for protein requirements, which is a very common situation.

This cow is now fed as follows, again 'Maintenance' and 'Production' are taken separately mainly for ease of calculation.

	Feed	Where fed
Maintenance	Silage	Feed barrier
'Lead feed'	2 lb (0·9 kg) rolled barley	Feed barrier
1st gallon (4·5 l.)	silage + 4 lb (1·8 kg) rolled barley	Feed barrier
2nd ,,	silage + 4 lb (1·8 kg) rolled barley	Feed barrier
3rd ,,	4 lb (1·8 kg) compound dairy cake	Feed barrier
4th ,,	,,	Parlour
5th ,,	,,	Parlour
6th ,,	,,	Parlour
7th ,,	,,	Parlour

(1 lb = 0·453 kg)

Ten pounds (4·5 kg) of rolled barley (with minerals) is fed together with 4 lb (1·8 kg) of dairy cake at the feed barrier in two feeds. Sixteen pounds (7·2 kg) of dairy cake [8 lb (3·6 kg) per feed] will be fed in the parlour. This ensures that normally a cow can easily eat this amount in the parlour during milking without upsetting the routine which would be necessary if she had to remain in the parlour to finish her feed. Quite often at this stage in lactation, cows will not take this quantity, but will rely for at least some of their feed requirements by milking off their backs.

Actual feeding methods in parlours have been the subject of much recent work. Abreast parlours can tolerate fairly simple shovel systems, as this is adequate for the size of parlour and herd and sufficiently accurate with an experienced operator. Tandem parlours are fairly easily fixed up with a system, although a large number have reverted to the use of a feed barrow in the pit, which incidentally has the added advantage of holding more than one type of feed in different compartments, for example high protein cake for high yielders, barley meal for low yielders.

With parlour feeding, especially in quick throughput herringbones, the use of coloured tail tapes is possibly the simplest and best way of controlling feeding. The number and colour of tail tapes being related to the number of pulls, turns, scoops, shovels, etc, or to the position of the disc of a semi-automatic dispenser. One blue tape, for example, denoting 2 lb (0·9 kg) per feed, two blues 3 lb (1·4kg), one red 4 lb (1·8 kg) and two reds 5 lb (2·3 kg) and so on. These tapes can be changed as needed but once per fortnight is usually quite sufficient. A chalk board stating the amount to be fed per cow can be used. It is, however, only suitable for a relatively small herd.

Many herdsmen will of course claim that these aids are not necessary and that their memory is good enough, but there is no doubt that they are a great help, especially in the dim haze of 5·30 am after the local village carnival dance or Young Farmers' Club ball. They are of course ideal for relief milkers, where in fact he or she does not have to even identify the cow and then read the board, but merely follows the instructions on the tail.

One word of warning with tail tapes. If they are put on too tightly, which is very easily done, they act in the same way as rubber rings on lambs' tails—cut off the blood and nervous supply to the tail, and thus can very easily cause the tail to die and drop off from the point of taping.

ELECTRONICS IN THE PARLOUR

Many new sophisticated parlour feeders are now available and, although expensive, may be justified where very high yields are required in large herds, or where high throughputs of cows are required. As time progresses, and with electronics and computers entering every branch of agriculture, we shall no doubt see more and more of these systems. The simplest of these is the use of punched cards for each cow. Placed in a sensitive control unit, these cards then activate electric dispensers and cause them to deliver the correct already programmed amount of concentrates. A more complex system, at least complex in the eyes of a non-electronically-minded layman, is built so that the cow's number, or rather the cows' numbers in the line is dialled in sequence. A master control, away from the parlour, then activates the feeders. If a line of cows in the order, eg Nos. 79, 63, 7 etc, are in the parlour, the computer will have been programmed previously, usually for one week, to activate the feeders on dialling these numbers in sequence to deliver 8 lb (3·6 kg), 7 lb (3·2 kg) and 3 lb (1·4 kg) to these three cows, the amount varying in relation to their daily yield or steaming-up ration. The computer in this case also can be made to receive from the parlour the daily yield of the cows, by having a sensitive weighing device or flow meter fixed, and in fact can hold this information in its 'memory' for next week's computation of feed allocation. It will also store a 'running total' of the yield of each cow throughout the lactation.

LIQUID FEEDING

Another relatively new development is to supply the cow in the parlour with her feed in liquid form, or rather in a semi-solid 'slop' consistency similar to that for piped pig-feeding. Rationing becomes easier as the amount of slop can be controlled more easily than cake or meal, and it is claimed, in the short term at least, that cows eat this feed more rapidly. There are, however, problems in maintaining feed tubes, etc in a clean condition and in preventing rancidity which can very easily take place, and which very rapidly reduces palatability of the feed. It is similar to what happens when mangers with ordinary meal or cake are not kept clean.

COLLECTING YARDS

The design of the parlour including collecting yards needs special attention. Collecting yards should be designed so that there is 'full flow' into the parlour. Thankfully, the Milk and Dairies Regulations, which insisted on doors between parlour and collecting yards, have been changed. These doors were never used in any case in practice, other than on the day that the installation was officially inspected. The use of carborundum powder on floors to prevent slipping is very useful and costs very little if the carborundum is incorporated in the half dry concrete floor when it is laid.

Collecting yards should not have awkward corners or cul-de-sacs, as cows invariable get into these, which can then stop the flow of cows into the parlour. The circular collecting yard is eminently suitable, with the travelling 'back-up' gate that can be electrically driven, and which gently edges the cows into the parlour entrance as milking progresses. In a rectangular collecting yard, an 'electric dog' can be used, which acts in the same way and nudges the cows forward so that they enter the parlour more easily. The 'electric dog' must be used with care, as constant shocking of the cows makes them very jumpy and irritable.

A suspended 1″ (25·4 mm) diameter galvanised pipe, wound forward by an electric motor, or manually by handle attached to a thin wire rope, is ideal. This can be electrified by means of insulators incorporated in the suspending wires, with an electric fence unit fixed to the travelling bar. Even if it is electrified it need hardly ever be switched on; consequently, it does not upset the cows and yet is very effective in moving cows forward.

BULK MILK TANKS

Bulk milk tanks are expensive, but excellent schemes are in operation under which they can be hired or paid for over a suitable period of time, with preferential interest rates. The premium paid on the milk collected in bulk usually goes a long way towards paying for the cost of the tank, particularly if the tank is fairly full.

One of the problems that constantly faces a large proportion of producers is that as herds have expanded, tanks installed a few years previously have become too small for the herd. Relying on churn collection for the extra gallons at peak times is actively discouraged, and in 1974 the collectors insisted that this would be the last year when churns would be collected from bulk milk farms. By 1975, however, with a shortage of milk, they were very glad to obtain any milk in churns, although under the programme of all bulk collection by 1977, including the development of small vats for small herds, collection of milk in churns will cease.

It is 'penny wise, pound foolish' to install a bulk milk tank without automatic cleaning, as these systems, although expensive, are now most efficient. The maximum advantage is obtained in a busy time, for example, at silage or hay times, when it is a very unpleasant task to rush to milk, often a little late, and have to clean the tank before milking. Far better an automatic system which the milk tanker driver has switched on before leaving the farm.

ACCESS AND ROADS

The siting of the dairy and access roads to it is very important.

Bulk milk tankers are heavy and not the easiest vehicles to manoeuvre. A reasonable road, and in particular a good turning space, is essential—far better than being confronted daily with an irate tanker driver.

WASHING PARLOUR AND COLLECTING YARD FLOORS

Finally, the twice daily chore of washing the parlour and collecting yard floors may take far too long, and this job, although essential, cannot be described as being very productive. Although seemingly archaic, the use of a stiff broom and buckets, with water collected from an open tank, is probably in many instances the cheapest, fastest and most efficient system; the bigger the buckets, the more efficient the system, and it is the quick rush of water that is effective in removing the muck.

On my visit to New Zealand, I was particularly impressed by the cleanliness of their parlours, or milking sheds as they call them. Their system of washing is based on the use of low-pressure, high-volume washing equipment. High-pressure, low-volume jets are useless for washing floors, but effective in removing dung from walls and pipework.

Following my visit, we have installed a low-pressure high-volume system of floor washing at Frondeg. Water from our own supply is stored in a 600 gallon (2,727 litres) steel tank and filled automatically using a ball valve. The 2″ (50 mm) outlet is connected to a $\frac{1}{2}$ hp (0·37 kW) electric pump which delivers water along a main 2″ (50 mm) tube running the length of the parlour, well above cow height, and in which are incorporated three quick release outlets. (The first installation did not take into account the Hereford bull mounting the cows in the yard, and he succeeded in smashing the plastic connections on a few occasions). These quick coupling devices allow us to couple a length of about 15′ (4·5 m) of rubber flexible hose, again 2″ (50 mm) in diameter.

Slurry is first scraped from the collecting yard—quite easily by a hand squeezee and pushed through a steel chute to a manure spreader. When this is full the slurry can be either spread on the land, or if wet or inconvenient, it can be spread direct to the main slurry lagoon. The floor can now be washed very quickly and efficiently with the high volume gush of water of 60 gallons (272 litres) per minute. An area of 1,000 sq ft (930 sq m) can be washed down in five minutes with very little effort. This reduces the herdsman's time, effectively makes this job a not unpleasant chore and keeps the floors absolutely clean.

Chapter 11

THE HEALTH OF THE
DAIRY HERD

I HAVE DISCUSSED the health of the herd in relation to production in several other chapters. This chapter is not meant to be an abridged veterinary text book, but is designed to deal with some of the common disorders of dairy cows and replacements, and their control by management; in fact their prevention, rather than their cure.

The veterinary profession exists primarily to help the producer maintain herd health. A veterinary surgeon would rather be called to the farm to discuss ways and means of preventing disorders, rather than to treat a sick animal. It is unfortunate that far too many vets are used as a 'fire brigade' to deal with disasters, rather than as 'fire prevention officers'. They are, however, often far too busy to give their time to discuss problems, and it is unfortunate that contract schemes, whereby vets visited farms on a regular basis, specifically to discuss herd health did not become popular. It is also highly significant that owners of many large herds employ veterinary surgeons full time, a large proportion of the time being spent in a consultative and managerial capacity.

The intelligent use of veterinary advice, together with managerial skills, can increase the production and profitability of a herd. If veterinary advice helps to control the following three disorders—mastitis, lameness, and infertility in a herd—its value in a 100-cow herd alone will be a very substantial sum.

MASTITIS CONTROL

We are all aware of the cow with one or more light quarters, and the lower yield from those quarters. If we add the total milk loss from this alone, the total in the national herd is enormous and costly in terms of lower production and profitability. A national mastitis control system is now available, based on white blood cell counts and body cell counts taken at monthly intervals throughout the year, which give a measure of the level of sub-clinical and clinical mastitis in the herd. An infected udder will try and 'fight' mastitis by the action of white blood cells, and the greater the incidence of the

121

disease normally, the greater the incidence of dead white cells and udder cells in the milk. In the first few weeks of lactation and again when drying off cows, cell counts can also be very high.

Cell counts are graded as shown in Table 6, and the loss of milk due to each level of infection, is also given in this table.

Table 6. Estimated Effect of Sub-Clinical Mastitis Infection on Loss of Milk Yield per Cow per Annum

Cell count per ml	Sub-clinical mastitis level	Estimated loss of milk per annum	
		Per Cow	Per herd of 100 cows
Less than 299,000	low	20 galls	2,000 galls
300,000–499,000	medium	50 galls	5,000 galls
500,000–699,000	medium high	75 galls	7,500 galls
700,000–999,000	high	150 galls	15,000 galls
1,000,000 or more	very high	200 galls or more	20,000 galls

(1 gallon = 4·54 litres)

The higher the cell count, the more likely is the herd to contract clinical, rather than sub-clinical, mastitis infections, and the heavier the toll on milk and money lost by the infected herd. The seriousness of the situation can be judged by the fact that the national average cell count for February 1975 was 583,000 cells per millilitre, and this in dairy herds where actual counts were taking place. This represents in annual loss of some 60–70 gallons (272·7–318·2 litres) of milk per lactation per cow in these herds due to mastitis. The control of clinical infection is veterinarians' work.

The control of sub-clinical mastitis can be successfully based on good husbandry and herd management, by the following methods.

1. Use of teat dips prevent infection through the teat canal after milking.
2. Culling of chronic or incurable cases. Some cows will not respond to veterinary treatment, but will regularly have clots in their milk and are therefore always suspect as a source of new infection in the herd.
3. Use of a veterinary surgeon to advise on treatment of all clinical cases of mastitis.
4. Use of long-acting antibiotics at drying off, with veterinary supervision.
5. Regular checking of milking machines (irregular vacuum levels or too high or low vacuum) and avoiding overmilking can prevent the build-up of mastitis infection.

6. Use of monthly milk cell counts to monitor sub-clinical infection.

Maintaining a low cell count and controlling mastitis have the following results: there is less clinical mastitis, reduced veterinary and medicine bills, increased milk yields, and of course mastitis can cause an appreciable drop in milk quality. The use of antibiotics in a milking cow's udder means the discarding of valuable milk, and of course, with a healthy herd, one reason for culling, due to mastitis infection, can be eliminated.

GRASS STAGGERS, OR GRASS TETANY

Thousands of dairy cows die each year from grass staggers. They usually die without warning and it is therefore too late to give remedial treatment. The condition is associated with a fall in blood magnesium levels, which usually occurs in the first few weeks after turnout to grass in spring. A golden rule with grass staggers is: try and prevent its occurrence.

The cow has a large reserve of magnesium in the body, but cannot make this readily available. Therefore she must have a regular intake of magnesium from the digestive tract to the blood stream daily. In spring, milk yields normally increase when turned out to grass, and this itself increases the drain of magnesium from the blood stream. Spring grass is also very low in magnesium content, as compared with grass grown in the other seasons, and these two factors can often trigger off the condition.

Clinical Signs of Grass Staggers

Too often the only sign of grass staggers is a dead cow in a field, often in the morning when the herd is collected for milking. If we are lucky enough to be close at hand when the symptoms occur, there is often, but not always, time to give the cow some treatment. The cow will become nervous, twitches, walks unsteadily, and very soon this is followed by muscular spasms. She falls to the ground and convulsions of the head and neck follow. She turns her eyes deep in their sockets and can die within a few minutes, or more likely in about half an hour, unless treated.

I have described the 'rapid' type of staggers, but often a slower less instant type can develop. There is far less spasm; the cow gradually falls, after a period of increasingly less steady walking, and gradually goes into a coma.

Treatment of Staggers

Whilst it is essential to follow veterinary advice, there is often no time to call a vet in the time available. A subcutaneous injection of a magnesium and calcium salt preparation should be given, using a flutter valve. It is essential to have a good supply of this solution and the injection equipment sterilised and readily at hand as you have to act quickly when a cow goes down with staggers.

Prevention

Obviously, when one cow develops staggers in a herd, it is essential to treat all the others to provide protection. The feeding of magnesium supplements whether bought as specially formulated high magnesium cattle cake or a home-mix with calcined magnesite incorporated when mixed, is a very effective method. However, it can be expensive if the cows do not need supplementary feeding, other than as a magnesium carrier.

This feed should supply some 2 oz (56·5 gm) of calcined magnesite per day, as this provides a sufficient daily intake of magnesium. This daily intake is important as a cow has no way of storing *available* magnesium in her body tissues.

Another, but rather expensive, method of controlling staggers is to 'dose' cows with long acting magnesium alloy 'bullets'. These dissolve slowly in the rumen and release magnesium slowly to be absorbed into the animal body, and are usually fairly successful.

During the danger period, dusting of pastures with powdered calcined magnesite, sown at the rate of 14–18 lb per acre (15–20 kg per hectare) is very effective. Care must be taken to dust pastures evenly, as calcined magnesite is not very palatable, and dusted areas will be left ungrazed if part of the grazing area is left untreated. Frequency of dusting depends on method of grazing. With daily paddocks or strip grazing, the area used over a period of four or five days may be treated at once, while with a set-stocking method of grazing, the whole area should be treated every 8–12 days, depending on weather conditions, particularly rainfall.

In many areas, dolomitic or magnesium limestone is available. Using this product as normal lime treatment on the land ensures that levels of magnesium in grassland do not normally fall to dangerously low levels. On many farms where magnesium limestone has been used over a period of years, there has been no problem whatsoever with staggers.

It is well worth stressing that the use of a combination of nitrogen and potassium in spring can induce staggers. The nitrogen of course ensures rapid grass growth, which in itself at this time is instrumental in lowering magnesium levels. The additional luxury availability of potash salts depresses magnesium uptake by plants, and the combined effect can often be grass with dangerously low magnesium levels, sufficient to trigger off staggers in dairy cows, beef cows, and sheep.

MILK FEVER

Symptoms of milk fever, or hypocalcaemia, are often similar to those of staggers, and when we are confronted with a cow in a coma in a field it is often extremely difficult to diagnose from what disorder she is suffering. Milk fever, however, usually occurs within a few days of calving. When a cow calves, it is usual for the level of calcium in the blood to fall. This is due to the need for calcium for milk production, and also in part to the effect of hormones. If this calcium level falls too low, milk fever follows.

Clinical Signs of Milk Fever

As with staggers, the cow may get restless and even excited; her feet will paddle, and finally she will fall quite suddenly. This may be dangerous to the cow, as she may fall in the collecting yard, parlour, or worse still in a byre, where she may very easily neck or strangle herself. After falling, the cow becomes progressively more drowsy and eventually lies on her side, with her legs outstretched.

Treatment

Calcium borogluconate injected subcutaneously using a flutter valve, should be administered as soon as possible. If the cow does not respond to this, a vet should be called in, but if the cow is found in a coma, it is necessary to get immediate veterinary assistance. In the meantime calcium borogluconate should be given before his arrival. In severe cases, the vet may inject intravenously, but on no account should this be done other than by the vet, as there will be a high risk of introducing air bubbles into the blood vessel and the immediate death of the cow.

Prevention

Older cows are more susceptible to milk fever than heifers, and some farms, whether this is due to the breeding of the cows or their feeding, have more cases of milk fever than others. In some herds, all cows past their third lactations are given calcium borogluconate at calving or even before, as cows can often go down prior to or even under the stress of calving. This preventative measure does not always completely guard against an attack, but if there is an incidence, it is usually less serious. There is also evidence that feeding a high phosphate mineral before calving, and also an injection of vitamin D3 given a few days before calving, have both been successful in preventing milk fever.

ACETONAEMIA/KETONAEMIA

Every spring there are very many dairy cows which show symptoms of acetonaemia or slow fever. The incidence of this disorder depends on the management of the herd, the stage of lactation, and the feed regime of the herd. Acetonaemia often effects high yielders and heifers in their first lactation, particularly in the larger herd where the stress in a first calver is greater.   During lactation we are used to cows 'milking off their backs'. The cow's reserves that she has built up during her dry periods are being mobilised and used to produce milk. This is a perfectly normal procedure in most milking cows.

Milk contains a high proportion of milk sugars, and if insufficient feed, particularly energy-rich feed, is being eaten by the cow, she has to resort to 'manufacturing' these sugars from her own body reserves. The problem arises when the body tissues, fat, and even protein, have to be broken down at too high a rate.

One of the products of this breakdown are ketones, particularly acetone. These chemicals are normally excreted by the animal. If, however, there is a massive level of ketones in the blood, these cannot be excreted quickly enough, and their progressive build up in the blood causes ketosis.

SYMPTOMS OF ACETONAEMIA

A cow suffering from acetonaemia usually goes off her food. Her daily milk yield drops rapidly; she moves about slowly, and her coat becomes 'starey'. Usually, the typical sweet smell of acetone, similar to that of pear drops, can be detected in the breath and in her milk.

Treatment

Veterinary treatment of clinical cases includes the use of glucose precursor preparations, or glucose-stimulating hormones. The animal may recover quickly and regain her former milk yield, although very often she will have lost a considerable amount of flesh in the relatively short time she has been suffering. If possible, a very quick recovery can be obtained by turning the cow out to grass for a period each day. Even though there may be very little grass available, a small amount often has a magical effect in helping the cow recover. I mentioned earlier that much of the increased yield at turnout may be due to recovery of cows from sub-clinical acetonamia. To prevent further attacks, the cows that have suffered an acetonaemia attack should be offered a high energy ration. The use of molassine meal both as an appetiser and source of energy is effective. Increasing the cow's intake of feed by not offering mouldy, unpalatable or stemmy hay or poorly fermented silage, can be effective in aiding recovery. Avoiding having overfat cows at calving, or, worse still, underfeeding fit cows after calving, are also important management aspects if acetonaemia is to be avoided.

BLOAT

We are extremely lucky in the United Kingdom that the incidence of bloat is relatively small. The greater use of nitrogen in dairy pastures, with the consequent decrease in clover content of the sward, has contributed to the progressive decline in the incidence of bloat. Nevertheless, bloat can still occur, especially in early spring on fresh grass and when cows are grazing kale in the autumn, particularly if the stock break through the electric fence and gorge themselves. The increased price of fertiliser nitrogen and related increased use of clover, particularly red clover, Italian ryegrass mixtures (mainly for conservation, but also for grazing at some time of the year), may well see an increase in bloat problems. The disease could rise to the level of some 20 years ago, when red clover was very often used as a constituent of grass mixtures.

In New Zealand, with pastures containing a high proportion of white clover, bloat is a severe problem. And during the 'bloat season' many herds are dosed individually, twice per day, with a detergent. This is no easy job, yet many herds I saw seemed to accept this, and cows practically opened their mouths for the drenching gun. Alternatively, a detergent can be incorporated into the drinking water supply in the paddocks by means of an automatic dispenser.

The cows rumen relies on a process of fermentation for the digestion of feed. This process results in the formation of gases, which are normally belched by the cow. When bloat occurs, the gases form a froth or foam, which is fairly stable, and this prevents the escape of gases. The build-up of gases causes a fairly rapid increase in the size of the rumen, and the animal may die very quickly of suffocation, as the rumen wall presses against the lungs and prevents breathing. In the same way, heart failure may be caused, either directly by the pressure in the heart cavity or by the lack of oxygen supply to the heart due to difficult breathing.

Animals of all ages may suffer from bloat, and in the last three years I have come across three bull calves that continually suffered from this complaint for no apparent reason. In each case no successful treatment was possible. Although they were drenched frequently. A polythene tube introduced through the mouth into the rumen gave immediate and spectacular relief, but the condition occurred more and more frequently, the calves lost condition, and eventually had to be destroyed.

Treatment

As with calves, a stiff rubber or polythene tube can be pushed into the cow's rumen, although this is not easy with a fully grown cow. Dosing with a detergent, or oil such as linseed oil, or even milk or cream, may help to break the surface tension of the foam and release the rumen gases.

When the animal is in a serious condition, and there is little time available, it is sometimes necessary to tap the rumen using a trocar and canula or, if this is not readily available, a clean sharp knife. Gases will be released immediately and the animal will recover quickly with the minimum of ill effect if the puncture is made in time.

It is essential for every farmer or herdsman to ask a veterinary surgeon to pinpoint the exact, correct spot to puncture the animal, before he is confronted with having to perform this emergency operation. Puncturing should of course only be resorted to when all else has failed and the animal's life is in danger. Even then, your veterinary surgeon should be called as soon as possible.

Prevention

Cows should be introduced to a clovery sward gradually. On no account should they be put in such a sward after a period on grass while they are still hungry. It is commonsense to put them in a clovery pasture in the morning for the first few days so that they can be observed, rather than at night. It is best to start with an hour or so on the first day, gradually lengthening the grazing time. In early spring the use of some hay or straw helps to combat bloat, either left in racks or put under the electric fence with strip- or paddock-grazing.

When feeding kale, it should be introduced gradually in the same way, and great care should be taken with strip-grazing to avoid breakout and gorging.

FOOT TROUBLES

The problems of lameness due to muscle or joint condition are too varied in origin to discuss, and are very much part of the veterinary surgeon's regime. Many foot troubles and conditions are, however, very often controllable or prevented by good cow management.

FOUL IN THE FOOT

This disease has many names throughout the country. Usual

symptoms are swelling of the foot above the hoof and infection between the hooves. The animal is in intense pain. The condition is normally very easily treated and cured by the use of antibiotics, given under the direction of the veterinary surgeon, and recovery can often be dramatic.

OTHER CAUSES OF LAMENESS

Lameness can be caused by foreign bodies, nails and stones, penetrating the hoof and causing direct pain, and later infection. Damage can be caused to a heifer's feet in the rearing stage by keeping it too long in soft straw, preventing natural wearing of the hooves. Overgrown feet, and in particular 'corkscrew claw' can be inherited characters, and these cows should not be bred from. Overgrown feet can be controlled by regular foot trimming. If this is done soon enough, it prevents the condition becoming too advanced for effective treatment.

Overfeeding, followed by laminitis, can easily occur in high-yielding herds, and this condition must be watched carefully. There is no doubt also that a modern installation, where the cows feet are continually in slurry, does not help in maintaining healthy feet. Softening and undue wear of the feet can occur. New concrete, with a highly abrasive surface, can also cause wear in a cow's feet, and a new set-up very often has more than its share of foot troubles in the first year.

Prevention

Good management can go a long way towards prevention of foot troubles. There is no doubt that many of the problems are inherited, and to correct this it is advisable to use bulls that are sound on their feet and breed from families with good feet and legs. Better still, use a bull whose progeny have high ratings for good feet and legs, avoiding in particular 'heely' families who walk on their softer heels rather than squarely on the feet and are therefore more prone to damage, wear and infections.

Good roadways and yards, free from flints and stones that will penetrate the hoof, are essential. Regular trimming, either by oneself or by a professional, is necessary for overgrown feet. It is essential to have an efficient cow-handling crate, with a canvas cradle to take the weight off the animal's feet, when trimming. It could be very easily shared between farms in an area, and the benefit of good trimmed feet would very quickly justify its cost. Some units have installed foot baths at the entry to the collecting yard, or at the exit to the parlour. If this bath is not kept clean regularly, and the formalin or cooper sulphate changed regularly to maintain its strength, the bath is more likely to be a source of infection than a means of prevention.

HUSK OR HOOSE

This is a condition that, although fairly easily prevented, causes an enormous loss of animal production every year. Calves of 3 months to over 18 months can suffer badly from husk, and the characteristic coughing must be watched for very carefully in cattle of this age when at grass. A bad attack can cause severe coughing, loss of condition and can actually lead to the death of the animal, usually from secondary infections such as pneumonia.

Treatment

When husk is suspected, veterinary advice must be sought as soon as possible: Dung samples can also be taken to a veterinary investigation laboratory, to confirm husk larvae. Delay in commencing treatment can be extremely costly.

Prevention

There is no doubt that with husk, prevention is far better than cure, and indeed very much cheaper. If young stock are to be turned out to a 'clean' pasture, such as a new ley, or where cattle have not grazed for at least 12 months, there is little risk of husk infection. However, on many, indeed most, farms, whether because the same fields are used for young stock year after year, or because of the intensive nature of the farm, turning out and grazing throughout the season in 'clean' ground is not possible.

Calves that are over eight weeks of age can be 'vaccinated' using 'Dictol'.* The drug is in the form of individual phials of irradiated husk larvae. They are given as two oral doses, one month apart, before turnout to grass, making sure that the calves are not turned out for two weeks after the second dose. The calves usually cough after both doses, and it is during this period that they are building up an immunity to any lungworm larvae that they will encounter later in the year. It is often too dry in midsummer for larvae to hatch, and attacks of lungworm or husk are often seen in September and October.

Calves that have been vaccinated can infect pasture, so it is an added advantage, as far as is possible, that a new pasture is found for each crop of calves in succeeding years. The treatment seems costly at first sight, but having once seen the ravages caused by husk, I am sure that no one would hesitate to vaccinate his calves.

One disadvantage of vaccinating spring-born calves with 'Dictol' is that they cannot be turned out until late. A March-born calf has to be a minimum age of eight weeks before it can be vaccinated; the second dose is given one month later, and the calf cannot be turned

Trade name, Allen & Hanburys, London.

out for at least another fortnight. Consequently such a calf is at least three and a half months old before turnout in June, and this is extremely late. Calves that are turned out to clean pasture need not, however, be vaccinated.

STOMACH WORMS

As with sheep, one beast is the other's worst enemy, particularly young stock in an intensively-grazed situation. Older cattle over 18 months do not normally suffer from stomach worms, as they have usually developed a resistance by this age. This resistance may be considerably reduced if the cattle are underfed.

Younger cattle are, however, very susceptible to stomach worm infection. A heavy infestation in the gut can cause severe scouring and loss of condition.

As with husk, it is possible to provide 'clean' pasture for these animals. Worm eggs are passed in the dung of infected cattle, and then hatch according to the weather. The time required for hatching is often only two weeks in summer, but may be longer in spring and autumn. Some larvae will survive the winter and will provide the initial infection the following year, when the herbage to which they are attached, is grazed, the initial small infection of spring gradually builds up towards midsummer, and it is from this time that problems are caused.

Control

The provision of 'clean' pasture, a midsummer treatment with an antihelminthic drug, and another move to clean pasture can be very effective in maintaining a low infection level. If this is not possible, strict routine monthly antihelminthic treatment, by dosing or injection, should be carried out. Even though stomach worm build-up may never reach high levels, there is no doubt that the use of regular dosing techniques maintains animals' bloom and the growth rate of young grazing animals.

An adequate supply of good grass is essential, as underfed cattle are more vulnerable and suffer far more from an infection than well-fed cattle. Young calves born in spring at Frondeg have, in addition to good grazing, some 2–3 lb (0·90–1·35 kg) of barley-based feed while at grass. Not only does this maintain growth rate, but also indirectly helps resistance to stomach worms.

LICE

I did not realise the effect that a lice infestation could have on cattle until recently. At Tanygraig Farm we rear some 150 beef cattle per year in excellent old stone cattle courts. A constant watch has to be maintained, otherwise there is a quick build-up of lice on young cattle. As a matter of routine, we now dust these cattle in their sheds throughout the winter, and this is effective in their control.

One species of lice, which we have obviously got at Tanygraig, sucks blood and causes severe anaemia if allowed to continue. The cattle become restless, itchy, lose their hair and also lose condition very rapidly.

Cattle should be deloused when they are housed, and then as frequently as necessary. They may be sprayed or dusted, and the effect is well worth while to maintain thriving stock.

WARBLES

If all cattle in this country were treated for warbles for one year, they would completely disappear from our cattle population. Cows charging across fields with tails up cause a considerable drop in milk yield. An attack by the warble fly must be very painful for the animal, and of course the damage to the hide at pupa emergence is very great.

The application of a systemic dressing to the cow's back in October and November causes the death of the developing warble fly in the animal's body, as they emigrate from the point where the fly laid the eggs on the belly and brisket and upper legs—to the animal's back. A few may survive but they are easily killed before emergence in spring by spot treatment with an insecticide. A useful one to use is sheep dip.

LIVER FLUKE

In 1974 it was estimated that at least half the farms in the United Kingdom have cattle and sheep suffering from liver fluke, causing an estimated loss in milk and meat production of £50 million every year.

This widespread incidence of liver fluke has been recently realised by pharmaceutical companies. It has always been known that the higher rainfall areas in the west suffered from fluke, but there is a far more widespread incidence of the disease, as is discovered at slaughter in cattle livers in the east of the country.

Losses from liver fluke include condemned livers at slaughter, loss of thrift and liveweight gain and of course, in dairy cows, an unknown level of losses in milk production, both in quantity in milk quality and a decrease in cow fertility.

The liver fluke depends on two hosts: the cow or sheep, and secondly, the snail in damp pastures.

Control

The first very easy, if often impractical, way is not to graze wet areas or to fence them off. This may help, especially on dairy farms, but is not the only answer. The second method is to destroy the snail, *Limnoea truncatula,* by drainage or by the use of chemical molluscicides, which can sometimes be effective if they can be applied evenly over difficult terrain. Badly infected farms have had to resort to dosage of infected animals. Great care should be taken with this drenching, and a programme of drenching drawn up with the assistance of a veterinary surgeon, particularly when the cows are in milk or heavily in calf. In most situations, the use of one drench in January of each year is sufficient for adequate control, while on a badly infected farm far more frequent dosage, following veterinary advice, may be necessary.

MINERAL DEFICIENCIES

To give blanket advice on the requirements of most minerals is both difficult and indeed dangerous. In west Wales and many other areas, one of the most obvious deficiencies in young cattle is copper deficiency. With black cattle the development of brown, starey coats is common and often the loss of hair around the eyes of Hereford or Hereford cross cattle is a clear symptom, but even then the deficiency must be diagnosed by a veterinary surgeon.

Most herds do not suffer from deficiencies when adequately fed, but nevertheless the addition of mineral blocks or powder is a very useful precaution. The element that must be watched, particularly with dairy cows, is phosphorus or phosphate salts. Rarely is there a clinical phosphorus deficiency, but the use of high phosphate minerals (either as self-help mineral mixes or incorporated in rations) can help substantially with the fertility of the herd.

Chapter 12

THE VALUE OF RECORDS

ANY EFFICIENT BUSINESS must maintain standards of production, keep records and maintain both physical and financial control of the business, and plan and budget ahead, particularly when costs of inputs and outputs are changing rapidly.

The dairy farm is in the same position as any other business and the monitoring of inputs and outputs is extremely important, which means that careful records must be kept. It is difficult to believe that a very large proportion of farmers do not record cows' yields and instead adopt a 'hit and miss' plan. They hope that the net result will be satisfactory. Some of these producers are, in their own way, successful, but they are in that position mainly by accident, having either inherited land cheaply or have been well established for a long time, with low fixed costs applying to their farming operations.

There is no doubt that maintenance of records and costings is imperative to producers, especially when large capital expenditure and borrowing are involved. In this chapter the form and value of physical records are discussed, while financial records are discussed in Chapter 13, although of course both these types of records are closely connected.

The list given below enumerates the physical records necessary to assess and maintain the efficiency of a dairying enterprise:
1. Milk yield and milk quality.
2. Feedstuffs used.
3. Forage acres used.
4. Calving, bulling and service dates.
5. Records of progeny born, and their parentage.
6. Records of veterinary treatment.

MILK RECORDS

Both the level of daily milk yield of the cow throughout her lactation, and the total annual yield during her lactation, are important. Daily milk yield figures are very necessary for rationing the cow throughout the lactation. In winter, especially in herds with a relatively high dependence on concentrates, rationing is most important in relation to yield and stage of the lactation. In Chapter 6 'lead feeding' during the early part of the lactation was mentioned, and of course this is impossible unless individual cow yields are known.

In some herds, blanket feeding of cows is practised, each cow getting the same feed regardless of level of production. This invariably results in overfeeding of low yielders and underfeeding of high yielders, and in fact the very wasteful use of expensive concentrates, as it is the high yielders and newly calved cows that will show most reponse to concentrate feeding.

Daily milk yield figures can be obtained quite simply by recording once a month, which is usually sufficient. Fortnightly recording is more satisfactory for rationing, but with low labour availability, this is often not possible.

While daily management of the herd is very dependent on obtaining current milk yield figures, cumulative or annual milk yield figures for the herd, and for individual cows, are also extremely important in relation to herd management. It is only by obtaining these records that the herdsman or owner can get to know his cows really well, in relation to their milk yields and of course the quality of the milk that they produce.

Low yielders, whose yields fall well below the herd average, can be culled, or at least bulled with a beef sire, so that none of their progeny enter the herd. By these methods the production potential of the herd can be gradually improved. Without the aid of records it is very difficult to assess the true value of the cow. A cow that does not reach spectacular peak yields, but continues with a long steady lactation, often produces the highest yield per lactation. This is particularly true for heifers who very often have a longer lactation than cows and, after reaching a plateau, remain at this yield for a long time. A heifer that does not peak above 4 gallons (18·2 litres) a day will often achieve a lactation yield of 1,000 gallons (4,546 litres) in a normal standard lactation period of 305 days.

Many herds exhibit a 'second lactation drop', in that second calvers give a lower yield than first calvers. A heifer in its first lactation is often very easy to get in calf for the second time, early in this lactation, and often calves her second calf well within a year of her first calf. Normally, a heifer has a long lactation and may be left milking in the herd for too long and will therefore have too short a dry period. There is therefore no time to build up her reserves for the second lactation. She does not reach a high peak yield and often dries off prematurely, resulting in a lower yield in her second lactation.

Heifers, particularly those that have calved at a young age of around two years to two years three months, should be watched carefully. If they are to calve again within the year, they should, if possible, be dried after around 280 days. This also allows time for them to grow and put on flesh before the demands of the developing calf become too great.

In Frondeg we fell into the trap, in 1973, of allowing heifers that had calved in February to milk well on into December. These heifers were due to calve again in January of the following year. We can still pick out these cows in the herd, being small in size, as they did not grow in this critical autumn period, and on looking through their records, they achieved very disappointing second lactation yields.

One way of getting over this problem of second lactation drop, especially in herds that calve all the year round, is to allow some 13 months between the first and second lactation. This can be done with seasonal calving by calving heifers at two years ten months to three years, a month earlier than the cows. On calving their second calf 13 months later, the heifers now fall into the normal calving pattern of the herd. This system allows for a reasonable milk yield in the first lactation and gives time for rebuilding of reserves before the heifer calves her second calf.

However, it demands calving the heifers at nearly three years, which is obviously unacceptable in many herds.

MILK QUALITY

In the same way that cows are culled according to milk yield they often have to be culled in relation to milk quality. Many cows, although high yielders, often produce low butterfat and related solid content milk. It is as well to remember that 3·00 per cent butterfat milk is below the legal limit, and too many of these low-butterfat cows in a herd may result in milk unacceptable for sale. In the same way as with selection for milk yield, it is not advisable to breed replacements from these cows.

Milk quality can of course be corrected to some extent by correct and adequate feeding, particularly using high energy feeds, but without knowing individual milk quality, no correction can be made. Low butterfat and solid content are affected by sub-clinical mastitis, and this can be detected by individual sampling for butterfat. Although not as reliable as cell counts, this can be useful for detection purposes.

RESPONSIBILITY OF INDIVIDUAL MILK PRODUCERS

I believe very strongly that all milk producers should record their herds officially by means of the Milk Marketing Board's National Milk Records Scheme.

Latest figures available show that in 1974, only 861,000 cows or less than 30 per cent of the total national herd in 2,881,000 cows in England and Wales were officially recorded.

A very large proportion of these non-recorded herd-owners expect good bulls to be available for their herds through the artificial insemination services. It is difficult to comprehend how these non-recorders expect young bulls to be proven, and to be available eventually to benefit these herds. If every herd was recorded, it would be far easier to test bulls, in particular young bulls, and by testing more, the chances of finding outstanding bulls would be far greater. Non-recorders are benefiting from the others who are willing to pay for a recording service, but they themselves pay nothing towards the scheme.

Non-recorded herds should pay a far higher fee for inseminations than recorded herds, especially for proven nominated sires, and they should only be allowed the use of good tested bulls when the needs of milk-recorded herds have been fully satisfied.

THE BENEFITS OF MILK RECORDING

It is very interesting to note that in 1973/74 milk recorded herds averaged 1,009 gallons (4,580 litres) milk per cow per annum, while non-recorded herds averaged 880 gallons (3,995 litres). It is reasonable to assume that many of the most forward-looking and efficient producers will record their herds as an aid to management. On the other hand, with at least some of these herds, an increase in milk yields per cow is due to improved feeding, culling etc, which is a direct result of information gained by recording, and as such, an extra 129 gallons (585 litres) sold will show a handsome profit after deducting the modest cost of milk recording.

RECORDING FEEDSTUFFS USED

The recording of feed used is obviously very closely linked to milk recording on a daily or weekly basis, and of course with milk production costs, which will be discussed in Chapter 13.

Standards of feeding vary from herd to herd, in relation to the level of production expected. Table 7, produced by the Milk Marketing Board, groups herds in relation to yields. The table also shows concentrate usage per cow at each level of yield for all herds other than the Channel Island breeds.

Except for low-yielding herds, it is most interesting that a standard 3·5 lb (1·58 kg) of concentrate is used on average for each gallon (4·54 litres) of milk produced. Bearing in mind that 3·5–4·0 lb (1·58–1·81 kg) of concentrates is taken as a 'rule of thumb' guide, to

Table 7. Use of Concentrate Feeds in Relation to Herd Average*

Gallons per cow/year	Less than 700	700–800	800–900	900–1000	1000–1100	1100–1200	Over 1200
No of herds	95	191	366	525	394	205	57
Yield per cow/gallons	623	758	853	951	1043	1141	1249
Cwt/concentrates/cow	20·1	23·9	26·3	29·7	32·5	35·7	39·8
Concentrates/lb/gallon	3·7	3·5	3·5	3·5	3·5	3·5	3·5

(1 lb = 0·453 kg, 1 gallon = 4·54 litres)

*Craven, John and Willis, Peter. Better Management No.17, Winter 1974.

be sufficient for a gallon (4·54 litres) of milk, the initial reaction is surely that, with all the discussion revolving around grassland management, grazing systems, seeds mixtures, fertiliser used, silage and hay quality, a very large proportion of milk is still produced from concentrates. This in itself is a very sobering thought. On studying Table 7 it is obvious that we can go a very long way towards being more dependent on grass and grass products for milk production, and that good grass can be very profitably substituted for concentrates in the vast majority of herds, as distinct from the normal practice of substituting concentrates for grass.

These figures are of course averages, and many herds will be performing on a better level than this average. These figures represent 128,000 cows and are from producers who, at least, are prepared to record and cost their herds, whereas a very large number of farmers who do not record this information will not even know how efficient or inefficient they are.

Average figures are often deceptive, but each and every herd in this country must have an aim which must be better than 3·5 lb (1·38 kg) of concentrates for each gallon (4·54 litres) of milk produced. In fairness, a large number of producers achieve far better results than this. To put my own cards on the table, in the year ending December 1974, the Frondeg herd sold a modest 993 gallons (4,518 litres) from 100 spring-calving cows. We used 14·1 cwt (716 kg) of concentrates, half of which was rolled barley. This represents a concentrate usage of 1·59 lb per gallon (0·159 kg per litre).

STANDARDS TO AIM FOR

The following are reasonable standards to aim for in terms of concentrate usage related to milk produced:

Table 8. Milk Yield and Concentrate Usage

Milk yield (gallons/cow/year)	Concentrates (cwt/cow)	Concentrates (lb/gallon)
700	5	0·80
800	7½	1·12
900	11	1·36
1000	16	1·79
1100	21	2·15
1200	28	2·61

(1 lb = 0·453 kg)   (1 gallon = 4·54 litres)

These are good standards for a very wide range of milk producers. If a producer can achieve better than this, he will have a very good performance indeed. Many farmers will not be content with a 700-gallon (3,178 litre) yield and will demand higher yields often to satisfy themselves. Low yields have to be accompanied by low costs, and as we see from Table 8 a higher usage of concentrates can be tolerated as the yield increases. This is because a basic number of gallons are required to pay off basic costs, after which the extra gallons, provided they are produced economically, represent the 'profit' sector of the returns. Although each extra gallon demands a higher input in terms of concentrate costs, it is still profitable provided a reasonably low level of concentrate usage is maintained. Present price ratios of milk to concentrate allow also for higher inputs of concentrates as milk yield rises. Table 9, however, shows that high yields do not necessarily result from increased concentrate usage.

It is a reflection on our dairy industry that two-thirds of milk producers use over 25 cwt (1,270 kg) of concentrates per year and that nearly a quarter of the sample use 2 tons (2·02 tonnes) or more and still only manage to produce 1,040 gallons (4,727 litres) herd averages, with an enormous concentrate usage rate of 4·4 lb per gallon (0·44 kg per litre).

Table 9. Concentrate Usage and Milk Yields*

Concentrates (cwt/cow)	Less than 15	15–20	20–25	25–30	30–35	Over 35
Number of herds	63	152	321	464	376	437
Yield (gallons/cow)	743	811	891	932	985	1040
Concentrates used (cwt/cow)	11·9	17·9	22·6	27·5	32·3	40·8
Concentrates (lb/gallon)	2·0	2·6	2·9	3·4	3·7	4·4

(1 lb = 0·453 kg, 1 gallon = 4·54 litres)

*Craven, John and Willis, Peter. Better Management No. 17, Winter 1974.

Tables 8 and 9 also show that each herd has to adopt its own standard, and that recording of yields and inputs are most important to give an indication of the standards being achieved. If the aim is 1,000 gallons (4,546 litres) per cow, it is of no use at the end of the day to realise that over two tons (2·02 tonnes) of concentrates have been used. Results must be monitored throughout to make sure that the concentrate usage is around and preferably below, 16 cwt (812 kg) at this level of yield. Concentrates are expensive and can very easily erode profit margins if their use is not watched very carefully.

The relationship between milk yields and concentrate usage is by far the quickest way to spot good or bad results in a herd, in the early stages. Spot checks are useful, provided of course due note is taken of the stage of lactation the cows are in and of course the amount being fed for steaming up. As an example, in January 1975, at Frondeg, with only two cows having calved and yielding a total of 10 gallons (45·4 litres), we were using 700 lb (317·8 kg) per day of concentrate, mainly for steaming up. As a spot check this would result in a 700 ÷ 10 or 70 lb of concentrates per gallon (7·0 kg per litre) which is of course a ridiculous figure if the stage of lactation is not known.

COMPUTERISED HERD MANAGEMENT

The Milk Marketing Boards, as well as many commercial firms, have now developed very valuable and sophisticated systems of monitoring herd results, using computers. The English Milk Marketing Board's Herd Management Control Service (HMC) is based on data obtained from its own National Milk Records Service, and is a most reliable asset in that it produces predictions for the herd's performance on a continuous basis. Comparisons can be made of course simply between this year's and last year's performance on the farm without the use of sophisticated computers, but in so many herds calving patterns, methods of feeding, etc, change and therefore it is extremely difficult, in many instances, to say that the herd is performing better or worse than in previous years.

The most important question that always needs an answer is: Are the cows milking as near to the potential of my system of management? Predictions are most useful when daily yields are falling. The questions that are asked when yields are falling are: Is milk yield falling too quickly? Should it be dropping at all? How can I or should I correct this drop? Will arresting yield drop be economical? Of course we must always be in a position of even questioning yields when they are rising. Is the rise sufficient? Is it being maintained at a quick enough rate to achieve peak? Am I going to reach my target?

INFORMATION REQUIRED FOR PREDICTIONS

Herd management control is based on the fact that much lactation data is available from many years' recording by the National Milk Records. Lactation curves were therefore available and thus individual lactation curves for each cow in the herd can be predicted quite accurately provided the following basic data is available to the computer:

1. Last calving date.
2. Total yield since calving.
3. Next calving date (last service date).
4. Lactation number.
5. If the cow is recently calved, her previous calving date (calving index).
6. Length of her previous lactation.
7. Yield recorded during her previous lactation.

Heifer yields are predicted on the basis of herd average until they have been milking for 80 days, after which sufficient information is available from their own lactations to predict their yields. By transferring the information to the computer, programmed to predict yields for each cow, total daily or weekly yields can easily be calculated.

Table 10 shows a typical computer printout for part of a herd of seven cows.

READING THE PRINTOUT

Cow No. 14 was due to calve on 7th May 1973, and was predicted to give 12,939 lb (5,877 litres) in her next lactation. In Week 32 she is due to give 65 lb (29·5 litres) per day, building up to a peak of 75 lb (34·1 litres) per day in Week 36, thereafter following a normal lactation curve with a cumulative $2\frac{1}{2}$ per cent drop in yield per week.

Cow No. 28 has given 13,044 lb (5,928 litres) in her last lactation and is due to dry off on June 30th. She is due to calve again, according to her service data, on August 25th and predicted to yield 12,925 lb (5,874 litres). Reading her line, we see that she should be dried off and have an eight-week dry period before calving again in Week 47.

THE CONSULTING OFFICER

The Consulting Officer will visit the farm as soon as possible after the next recording, and as near to that date as possible. He will check any discrepancies, record that each predicted event—calving, drying off, etc—has happened, and correct for changes, as well as make any corrections for sales of cows, buying of cows, or transfer in or buying of heifers.

When he has obtained this information he will continue the line of prediction for the next ten weeks.

The farmer or herdsman will have plotted weekly milk production against prediction up to the visit of the consulting officer. Ideally, if all is going well, the two lines (predicted and actual) will coincide, but often they do not. Changes may be easily explained—lack of grass, poorer quality silage than expected, mastitis, low-level

Table 10. Typical Computer Printout of Milk Marketing Board's Herd Management Control Computer*

LIST OF COW DATA WITH PREDICTED DATES AND LACTATION YIELDS

HERD NUMBER 61/806/00/1 DATE 15/04/73

COW LINE NO	LACT NO	CALVING DT	YIELD	DRYING OFF	NEXT CALVING DT	NEXT YIELD	MONITOR AT 13/05/73	NOTES
14	11	18/04/72	12746	09/03/73	07/05/73 -	12939	0	
20	10	31/07/72	12462	19/05/73	14/07/73 -	12543	3	
28	10	07/09/72	13044	30/06/73	• 25/08/73	12925	3	
30	7	30/11/72	11311	01/10/73	26/11/73	11580	2	
88	11	29/09/72	11097	08/07/73	02/09/73	11581	2	
94	6	30/01/73	12975	14/11/73	• 09/01/74	13224	2	
97	8	07/01/73	13227	26/10/73	• 21/12/73	13393		

LIST OF INDIVIDUAL WEEKLY PRODUCTION OVER 20 WEEKS FROM FORECAST DATE (LBS/DAY)

HERD NUMBER 61/806/00/1 DATE 15/04/73

COW LINE NO	WK29	WK30	WK31	WK32	WK33	WK34	WK35	WK36	WK37	WK38	WK39	WK40	WK41	WK42	WK43	WK44	WK45	WK46	WK47	WK48
14				65.8	73.1	75.2	75.6	75.0	73.7	72.1	70.2	68.0	65.8	63.5	61.2	58.8	56.5	54.1	51.8	49.6
20	21.0	20.5	15.4	10.3	5.1								67.0	72.9	74.8	74.9	74.1	72.6	70.8	68.7
28	28.6	28.0	27.4	26.7	25.4	24.3	23.1	17.4	11.6	5.8									69.2	75.1
30	40.5	39.8	39.1	38.1	36.5	34.9	33.3	31.8	30.4	29.0	27.6	26.3	25.1	23.9	22.7	21.6	20.6	19.5	18.6	17.6
88	30.8	30.2	29.6	28.8	27.5	26.2	25.0	23.8	17.9	11.9	6.0									
94	62.5	61.9	61.1	60.4	59.1	56.8	54.5	52.3	50.1	47.9	45.8	43.8	41.8	39.9	38.1	36.3	34.6	33.0	31.4	29.8
97	58.1	57.3	56.4	55.6	54.3	52.1	49.9	47.8	45.7	43.7	41.8	39.9	38.0	36.3	34.6	32.9	31.4	29.9	28.4	27.0

*Clothier, Richard. Better Management No. 11. Summer 1973.

acetonaemia—when 'actual' is below 'prediction'. On the other hand a brighter picture is indicated when more milk than predicted has been produced due to better management, better grass, higher feed inputs, etc. In a *good grass year* actual yields may be better than expected for no apparent reason, which is one of those rewarding times in farming, all too infrequent, when you get more than you expected.

INTERPRETATION OF RESULTS

The first stage of interpreting the result is to look at total production and compare this with the predicted total. The next stage is to look at three groups of cows as follows:

Group 1. Early lactation cows—the most sensitive.
Group 2. Mid-lactation cows.
Group 3. Late lactation cows—the least sensitive.

These groups are looked at very critically. Peak yield not being achieved in Group 1 may reflect heavily on the rest of the lactation, and cows underfed at this period will not only yield well below prediction, but will lose flesh rapidly and may therefore be difficult to get in calf. Changes in rations and amounts fed have to be looked at carefully, when discussing these results, and also—a most important point—the economics of correcting feeding discrepancies, and the return expected, have to be borne in mind.

INDIVIDUAL COWS

A more detailed look can now be taken to see how individual cows are performing in the herd. From Table 10 we can ask the question, 'Is Cow No. 14 peaking at 75·6 lb (34·3 litres) per day or is she short of her peak or has she peaked at a higher level?' This information will give an indication of the feeding level of the cow in particular.

There will obviously be many discrepancies between individual cow predictions and actual yields obtained—for example, a cow bulling on recording day or mastitis—but if a large number of cows are well below prediction, particularly in cows in early lactation (Group 1), then the feeding system should be looked at very critically.

The use of this system, either through the services of the Milk Marketing Board or commercial firms, is invaluable in monitoring performance, and as an 'early warning system' if things are going wrong. It is the first time that full use has been made of milk records, not as historical figures to be looked at after the event, but as very useful current management data, from which decisions of a short- or long-term nature can be made.

CALVING, BULLING AND SERVICE DATES

On any dairy farm it is absolutely essential to maintain these records as basic information. Many boards—rectangular, circular, magnetic, wired or stringed—have been designed to aid this recording and these aids are very valuable, particularly as herds get larger.

Any system must satisfy the following:

1. It must give a clear indication of when cows are calving.
2. It must also allow the herdsman to read at a glance, when to dry off and steam-up prior to calving.
3. It must draw attention very clearly to a cow that has not been bulling or been served after some eighty to ninety days after calving.
4. It must also draw attention to cows that are continually being served, and are therefore not conceiving.

National Milk Recording sheets now provide an excellent 'events' column which is invaluable for the herdsman as a further reminder. An example of this is given in Table 11 (page 146). By entering the cow's drying off, calving and service dates, the computer printout will print either (a) the date of next calving, or (b), if after 84 days the cow has not been served, the word 'EMPTY'. This gives ample warning that if this cow is to calve her next calf with a reasonable calving index, steps must be taken to spot her bulling, or to seek veterinary advice to ascertain whether she is suffering from an infected uterus, cystic ovaries or another problem, which may of course be simple malnutrition.

From Table 11 it is seen that Cow No. 1 (M Elsie 3rd) is due to be served in Week Four and Five, Cow No. 2 (Madeline) has already been calved 91 days and service is due next time she is seen on heat.

Cow No. 3 (Pauline) has been calved 104 days. She was served on 8 October 1974 and a pregnancy diagnosis is due (if this is carried out in the herd normally) in Week Three, that is, the first week in December.

Cow No. 4 (Amy) is due to calve on 24 January, 1975, and should be dried off in Week Two (24 November 1974). Cow No. 5 (M Anne 2) has been dry since 18 October, 1974, and is due to calve on 21 December 1974, as is shown in event column and in Week Five of the action list. Susan (No. 6) has been dry since 24 September 1974 and is due to calve on 25 November 1974, while Kay (No. 7) calved on the 11 January 1974, was never served, as the word 'EMPTY' appears; she of course left the herd as a barren cow on 29 October 1974.

This example shows the value of the computer printout, and the use of the milk recording service as a management aid.

Table 11. Typical Milk Marketing Board Monthly Statement of Milk Records Printout*

SCHEME MRS
SEQUENCE   SHEET

MR S HERD
RECORDS FARM
THAMES DITTON
SURREY

MONTHLY STATEMENT OF MILK RECORDS
MILK MARKETING BOARD
THAMES DITTON, SURREY.

DATE OF LAST WEIGHING 30/31-10-74

PERIOD ENDING DATE 17-11-74

HERD No XX/12345/1
DATE OF YOUR NEXT WEIGHING 02-12-74
NATIONAL HERD MARK BX 909
BREED PREFIX

F MILK RECORDS

CALVING DATE	LACT No	LACTATION TO PERIOD END'G DATE				TESTS		FIELDS	BREED	IDENTITY No	NAME OF ANIMAL
		YIELD	DAYS	FAT%	PROT%	FAT%	PROT%				
24 10 74	03	1200	24	3·88	4·01	1	47	48	F	9871234	1 M ELSIE 3
18 08 74	03	2408	91	4·62	3·85	2	111	92	G	BX909/15	2 MADELINE
05 08 74	02	3541	104	4·83	3·27	3	171	116	A	BX909/18	3 PAULINE
04 10 73	02	11839	305	4·28	3·18	10	507	376	F	9875061	4 M AMY 2
		14740	409	4·32	3·25	13	637	479			
03 01 74	02	16514	288	3·73	3·03	9	617	500	F	9896331	5 M ANNE
23 10 73	01	DRY	(24-09-74)						F	BX909/36	6 SUSAN
11 01 74	01	8964	291	3·78	3·20	9	339	287	F	BX909/41	7 KAY

LINE No	LAST WEIGHING				EVENT	DATE	SEE NOTES BELOW
	YIELD	FAT%	PROT%				
001	50	3·88	4·01		CALVED H		S (12 12 74)
002	22	4·04	3·70				
003	22	4·39	2·94		SERVED(1)	08 10 74	15 07 75
004	23·5	4·73	3·59				24 01 75
C 005					DRY	18 10 74	21 12 74
006							25 11 74
C 007					LEFT HERD	29 10 74	EMPTY

ACTION LIST
WEEK BEGIN DATE
1 - 17 11 74
2 - 24 11 74
3 - 01 12 74
4 - 08 12 74
5 - 15 12 74

LINE No	WEEK No 1	2	3	4	5
001				S	S
002	S	S	S		
003			P		
004	D				
005					C
006		C			
007					

*Hawker, John. Better Management No. 17 Summer 1973.

HEIFER CALVES

A record of the parentage of heifer calves is essential if information on the breeding value of bulls used is to be collected, particularly as this data can be beneficial in choosing bulls suitable for any particular farm and system of dairying. This recording need not be elaborate. We have used coded ear tags as seen in photo 3. The year of birth, or in our case the year of calving, can be coded—5 (calved her first calf in the spring of 1975); similarly all the 400's calved in 1974. The name of the bull is also inscribed, for example, IA *(Ironside Alphonso)* and the name of the dam can also be included if necessary. Possibly for most herds the first figure could coincide with the year of birth—600's in 1976 etc—and a series of colours can be used to denote different bulls. The value of being able to distinguish sire groups from a young age is invaluable, and enables the herdsman or farmer to get to know young stock from a very early age. Bulling dates can be recorded, even though the heifers may be running with the bull, and this information is important when preparing heifers for calving.

RECORDS OF VETERINARY TREATMENT

Veterinary treatment, both professional services and the use of medicines, can amount to considerable costs. If a record is kept of all treatments, the cows that need attention often can be identified. A record card for each cow is the ideal method, especially in larger herds. In smaller herds the man in charge can usually remember each cow's problems.

Cows that suffer continually from mastitis are usually carriers and spread mastitis through the rest of the herd. When records denote recurrent attacks, the cow should be culled.

Chapter 13

FINANCIAL RESULTS OF THE DAIRY HERD

THERE IS NO value in discussing husbandry practices and techniques, feeding regimes, time of calving, disease control, etc, if at the end of the day the system adopted is not profitable. Whether this profit has been commensurate with the amount of capital involved and expertise used, and also the effort put into dairying, will be a subject for discussion for a very long time.

It is extremely difficult to discuss financial results at any period of time, with continual changes in milk prices, inflation, and rises in cost of raw materials and services, and I realise fully that figures quoted for 1975 may be outdated and meaningless in 1977 in terms of production costs and returns. As an example of variations in returns, in 1974/75 the value of a good Friesian bull calf has varied between £50–£60 at a fortnight old to as low as 50p or less. The cull cow market has in the same way varied enormously, and it is these dramatic fluctuations that make predictions extremely difficult, not to mention making farming also very difficult.

The aims of this chapter are to examine present-day production systems in term of inputs, outputs and returns, and to compare various systems, relating physical inputs to physical and financial outputs.

The most comprehensive source of information on dairy costings is produced by the Milk Marketing Board, Low Cost Milk Production Services (LCP). Table 12 is a summary of LCP report for the period March 1973 to April 1974. Some of the figures will be well out of date, and I have added estimated 1974/75 figures for comparison. Table 12 will also serve as a basis in discussing the important factors involved in determining the efficiency of any dairy farming system.

By sheer chance my predicted gross margins per cow and per acre for 1974/75 have worked out to be identical, using current figures with the LCP overall average for 1973/74, although all costs and returns have risen considerably.

The average size of LCP recorded herds is sixty-six cows compared with an England and Wales national average of thirty-nine

Table 12. Average results of LCP Recorded Herds 1973/74, together with Estimated 1974/75 Results (all Herds other than Channel Island Herds)*

	Top 25%	Bottom 25%	Overall average	Overall average 1974/75 (Author's predictions)
No. of herds	471	426	1,813	
Physical Results				
Herd size	73	57	66	—
Yield—gall/cow	1,035	836	945	945
Concentrates—cwt/cow	30·8	28·1	29·5	29·5
Concentrates—lb/gall	3·4	3·7	3·5	3·5
Stocking rate—acre/cow	1·0	1·7	1·3	1·3
Nitrogen use—units/acre	162	81	123	—
Financial Results				
Output £				
Value of milk	228	178	205	287
Calves less depreciation	38	28	34	10
Total	266	206	239	297
Variable costs £				
Concentrates	73	66	70	112
Purchased roughages	4	4	3	6
Forage	16	15	15	15
Sundries (vet, etc.)	12	11	12	12
Total	105	95	100	158
Gross margin per cow	161	111	139	139
Gross margin per acre	167	65	113	113

*Craven, John and Willis, Peter. Better Management, Winter 1974, No. 17.

cows, Scotland with an average of sixty-six cows and Northern Ireland with eighteen cows. The size of the national average herd has grown steadily over the years, and particularly in the last few years, at about an average rate of 2·5 cows per herd per annum. The belief has been widely held that as herd sizes increased, particularly as they reached the 100 plus mark, that this would result in lower performance per cow. This is undoubtedly true in some instances, where the expertise necessary to manage large herds is not available, but surprisingly perhaps, again from LCP results, the results both physical and financial do not show any detrimental effect for large herds compared with smaller herds. In fact the opposite is true, as is shown in Table 13.

Table 13. Average LCP Results according to Herd Size (other than Channel Island Breeds)*

Herd Size	Under 50	50–100	100–200
No of herds	659	902	241
Physical Results			
Herd size	37	70	126
Yield—gall/cow	921	952	983
Concentrates—cwt/cow	29·3	29·8	29·1
Concentrates—lb/gall	3·6	3·5	3·3
Stocking rate—acre/cow	1·4	1·3	1·2
Nitrogen use—units/acre	99	128	167
Financial Results			
Total output £	232	241	248
Total Variable Costs £	97	101	103
Margin over concentrates £	129	137	146
Gross margin per cow £	135	140	145
Gross margin per acre £	105	115	127

*Craven, John, and Willis, Peter. Better Management, Winter 1974, No. 17.

Larger herds achieved a significantly higher yield per cow, yet used the same amount of concentrates and therefore less concentrates per gallon of milk produced. The larger herds were more intensive, their margin over concentrates figure was greater, as was gross margin per cow and per acre. Provided the operator and owner realise that large herds have problems, more than twice the intensity of problems with a 100-cow than with a 50-cow herd, it is quite possible to maintain or even increase performances as a herd becomes larger.

YIELD PER COW AND MARGIN OVER CONCENTRATES

These factors are both very important, particularly when data regarding stocking rates and concentrate usage are available. In Table 12 LCP figures show an average yield of 945 gallons (4,294 litres) sold per cow with the top 25 per cent of herds averaging 1,035 gallons (5,114 litres). As was discussed earlier, however, the average figure of 3·5 lb per gallon (0·35 kg per litre) is far too high. It is reasonable to assume also that the true national average is far greater than this, as at least LCP recorded herds know what they are feeding, while others have no idea, and many would have a very rude awakening if they started recording.

'Margin over concentrates' is a quick, easy and very useful figure to compare herd performance: 1,000 gallons (4,546 litres) sold per cow at 31p per gallon (6·9 p per litre) gives a total milk sale figure per cow of £310. If 16 cwt (80·3 kg) of concentrates at an average price of £75 per ton (£76 per tonne) are used, the total concentrate bill is £60 and the margin over concentrates is £310 minus £60 or £250.

Similarly, a high-yielding herd, selling 1,300 gallons (5,910 litres) of milk and using 42 cwt (2,133 kg) of concentrates will achieve the following results:

Value of milk sold per cow	Value of concentrates fed	Margin over concentrates
£407	£157	£250

The question arises immediately of course 'Is it worth feeding these concentrates?' It is far easier to obtain a figure of 1,000 gallons (4,546 litres) sold using 16 cwt (80·3 kg) of concentrates than to push the herd to 1,300 gallons (5,910 litres) and use 2 tons (2 tonnes) of concentrates, to achieve exactly the same results in terms of margin over concentrates. This is an extremely important indicator figure in this context, as all that the high producer is really doing is supporting feed companies, and at the same time landing himself with a more difficult and a higher yielding herd to manage. The future will dictate whether the feeding of concentrates is profitable, or even possible, in terms of world feed supplies and availability of products that can be used directly as human food, rather than their more wasteful use for double processing into human food through the animal.

LCP results as given in Table 14 (page 152) again show the relationship between milk yields per cow and concentrate usage.

I must stress that these are average figures for a large number of herds, but it is most interesting that the margin-over-concentrate figure varied very little indeed. Of course it can be argued whether herds averaging only 743 gallon (3,376 litres) should be using 11·9 cwt (504 kg) of concentrates, and of course at the other end of the scale it is a sad thought that cows being fed 2 tons (2 tonnes) of concentrates can only just pass the 1,000 gallon (4,546 litres) milk scale figure.

STOCKING RATE

This is of course a figure that is far more easily calculated on an all-grass farm than on a mixed arable grass farm where arable by-products often contribute to production. From Table 12 it is seen that the best 25 per cent of LCP recorded herds are stocked at an average rate of 1·0 cow equivalent per acre (2·5 cows per hectare), while the bottom 25 per cent can only achieve one cow equivalent per 1·7 acres (1·4 cows per hectare). This is further reflected in the fertiliser used in

Table 14. Average Results of LCP Recorded Herds 1973/74. Analysis by Concentrate Usage Groups (Herds other than Channel Island Breeds).*

Concentrates cwt/cow	Less than 15	15–20	20–25	25–30	30–35	Over 35
No. of herds	63	152	321	464	376	437
Physical Results						
Yield—gall/cow	743	811	891	932	985	1,040
Concentrates—cwt/cow	11·9	17·9	22·6	27·5	32·3	40·8
Concentrates—lb/gall	2·0	2·6	2·9	3·4	3·7	4·4
Stocking rate—ac/cow	1·5	1·4	1·4	1·4	1·3	1·3
Nitrogen use—units/ac.	109	111	117	124	131	123
Financial Results						
Margin over concentrates £	127	132	138	136	137	133
Gross margin per cow £	129	135	142	140	140	135
Gross margin per acre £	95	102	113	113	117	115

(1 lb = 0·453 kg   1 gallon = 4·54 litres   1 acre = 0·404 hectare)

*Craven, J. A. and Willis, Peter. Better Management, Winter 1974, No. 17.

these groups, in that at one end 162 units of nitrogen are used, while at the other only 82 units of nitrogen are used.

When comparing farms, particularly their stocking rate, the quality of the land must be taken into account, together with rainfall, height above sea level, and often how long it has been in the hands of the operator. As a general guide, achieving one cow per forage acre (2·5 cows per forage hectare) is an excellent achievement, provided of course this area also produces fodder other than concentrates for the herd, and that the use of concentrates is not disproportionally high.

A good standard is a stocking rate of one cow per acre (2·5 cows per hectare) and 1,000 gallons of milk sold per acre (11,330 litres per hectare). This figure can be most deceiving, however, as it does not take into account the weight of concentrates used, for which a 'correction factor' must be applied as follows:

EXAMPLE A (Metric equivalents are not included for clarity)
Stocking rate = 1·0 cow per acre. Milk sold = 1,000 gallons/cow.
Apparent: Milk sold per forage acre = 1,000 gallons.
Concentrate used = 16 cwt (equivalent to ½ acre of barley at an average yield of 32 cwt/acre).
Total acres used = 1 (grass) + 0·5 (concentrate equivalent) = 1·5 acres.
    True total milk sold per acre 1,000 ÷ 1·5 = 666 *gallons*.

EXAMPLE B
Stocking rate 1 cow to 1·3 acres. Milk sold = 1,300 gallons per cow.
Apparent: Milk sold per forage acre = 1,300 ÷ 1·3 = 1,000 gallons.

Concentrates used = 42 cwt.
Barley equivalent = 42 ÷ 32 = 1·6 acres.
Total acres 1·3 (grass) + 1·6 (concentrate equivalent) = 2·9 acres.
Milk sold per acre 1,300 ÷ 2·9 = 448 gallons.
True total milk sold per acre = *448 gallons*.

(1 lb = 0·453 kg   1 gallon = 4·54 litres   1 acre = 0·404 hectare)

These two examples show that great care must be taken in interpreting farm results. In fact the true milk sold per acre may become increasingly important with scarcity and shortage of bought concentrate feed.

NITROGEN USE

It is surprising that even with high stocking rates of 1 cow per acre (2·5 cows per hectare) in Table 12 (page 149), only 162 units of nitrogen per acre (405 units per hectare) were used. Normally, some 200 units+ per acre (500 units+ per hectare) are needed for stocking rates of this level. Nitrogenous fertiliser is also another expensive raw material, but applying a 'correction factor' for this is far more difficult than with concentrates. The use of more clover as a natural source of nitrogen in grassland, and possible reduction in stocking rates, may well be forced on producers due to economic pressures. Indeed the commodity itself, bearing in mind that its manufacture is based on the use of fossil oils, will obviously be limited in its availability in future.

HERD DEPRECIATION

Herd depreciation is calculated quite simply as follows:

Herd depreciation =	value of cows or heifers transferred into herd	*minus*	value of cull cows sold	*minus*	value of calves sold or transferred

This implies of course that the value of herd is kept static, or is changed by minimal amounts, otherwise this will not only markedly affect herd depreciation or appreciation, but will only serve to produce paper profits or losses.

Calf and cull cow prices have fluctuated so dramatically recently that it is difficult to give figures that will be meaningful for the future.

Herd depreciation depends to a large extent on the number of heifers or bought cows entering the herd every year, which is of course dependent, in a stable sized herd, on the average productive life of the cows in the herd—in fact on how long cows last as viable producers within the herd.

Culling rate will vary between herds due to many factors, and also within the same herd for different years. The use of a bad bull with daughters developing, for example, bad feet after three lactations, may result in a very heavy culling rate for a few years. The use of a series of good bulls with daughters sound in feet, udder and capable of high yields may result in very low culling rates.

The average working life for a cow in the national herd is around four lactations, that is a culling rate of 25 per cent. This means that some 25 new heifers or cows have to enter a 100-cow herd every year. If this culling rate was reduced to 20 per cent only 20 heifers are needed per year, and similarly only 17 heifers if the average working life could be increased to six years.

Culling and replacement rates therefore have a marked effect on the herd depreciation, but this again is related to cull cow prices. When cull cow prices are high, a high culling and replacement rate has a relatively minor effect on the depreciation figure for the herd. If cull cow prices are low, the cost of culling is far greater.

As examples we will consider a 100-cow herd with a normal 25 per cent replacement rate. The cost of a heifer at calving is taken as £200 (see Chapter 4). Table 15 gives typical herd depreciation costs for three recent periods.

Examples A, B and C in Table 15 give reminders of the ups and downs of a dairy herd, and the reasons why the quoting of standard figures is very difficult.

From Example A it can be seen that reducing the culling/replacement rate has a relatively small effect on herd costings. In both the other examples, however, heavy culling has a far greater effect. In addition, of course, the higher the replacement rate, the greater the proportion of heifer lactations in the herd. As heifers usually have a lower yield than a mature cow, this can decrease total milk sales considerably.

VARIABLE COSTS

I am no prophet, but I have to assume that concentrate prices will remain or increase from their present value of £70–£80 per ton (£70–£80 per tonne). The costs will certainly not be reduced in the foreseeable future. Costs of veterinary services will in all probability increase, as will all other costs. Little more can be said, other than these costs must be watched very carefully.

Table 15. The Effect of Cull Cow and Calf Prices on Herd Depreciation/ Appreciation Costs of a 100 Cow Herd

A. July 1975

Expenditure		*Income*	
Transfer in of 25 heifers @ £200 =	£5,000	24 cull cows @ £100 =	£2,400
		90 calves @ £20 =	£1,800
Total	£5,000	Total	£4,200

TOTAL herd depreciation = £5,000 *minus* £4,200 = *minus* £800
Depreciation per cow in herd = *minus* £8.

B. August 1973 Calf prices and cull cow prices were very high.

Transfer in of 25 heifers @ £200 =	£5,000	24 cull cows @ £160 =	£3,840
		90 calves @ £45 =	£4,050
Total	£5,000	Total	£7,890

TOTAL herd appreciation: £7,890 − £5,000 = *plus* £2,890
Appreciation per cow: *plus* £28·90.

C. October 1974 October 1974 gave a completely different picture; a time in fact when a large number of cows had to be sold from Frondeg.

Transfer in of 25 heifers @ £200 =	£5,000	24 cull cows @ £60 =	£1,440
		90 calves @ £8 =	£720
Total	£5,000	Total	£2,160

TOTAL herd depreciation: £5,000 *minus* £2,160 = *minus* £2,840.
Depreciation per cow: *minus* £28·40.

FIXED COSTS

At this stage I must mention fixed costs—costs of labour, power, machinery, rent, rates, bank charges, etc. These costs I cannot obviously ignore, but as mentioned earlier they are increasing so rapidly, that if discussed in detail here, will possibly be meaningless by the time this sentence reaches print. These are, however, extremely important and can at the moment total up to £75 fixed costs per acre (£185 per hectare). This means that a gross margin of twice this figure must be achieved to provide a reasonable return on capital and a reasonable level of profit.

Throughout this book I have frequently mentioned the Welsh Agricultural College's dairy farm at Frondeg. To end this chapter, I give a summary of the herd's records for the year ending December 1974 (Table 16). Our figures for a spring-calving herd are reasonable, with a margin over concentrates of £203 and a gross margin per cow and per acre of £170·53 (£420 per hectare). They are above the average of even the highest herds in LCP as given in Table 12. In the year January 1975 to December 1975, we had to resort to using some concentrates during the very dry summer. Milk sales per cow and heifer for Frondeg's spring calving herd reached 1,209 gallons (5,495 litres) with a concentrate usage of 29 cwt (1,473 kg) giving a margin over concentrates of £296. As a reminder to ourselves, and many others that we have a long way to go, I also quote figures for Mr Edwin Bushby's autumn-calving herd in Cumbria (Table 17).

Table 16. Summary of Financial Results, Welsh Agricultural College Frondeg Farm (January 1974–January 1975).

	Whole herd	*Per cow*
Average number of cows	99·3	—
Milk produced	98,611 gallons	993 gallons
Value of milk produced	£25,253	£254·31
Concentrates fed per cow	70·15 tons	14·1 cwt
Cost of concentrates	£5,056	£50·92
Margin over concentrates	£20,197	£203·39
Cost of fertiliser per acre	£19·42	£19·42
Forage acres used	99·3	1·0
Concentrates used per gallon	1·59 lb	

Summary per acre and per cow (stocking rate 1·0 acre per cow).

Value of milk produced	£254·31
Value of calf	£37·00
Herd depreciation	*minus* £28·12
Total output	£263·19
Total variable costs	£92·66
GROSS MARGIN per acre	£170·53
GROSS MARGIN per cow	£170·53

(1 lb = 0·453 kg   1 gallon = 4·54 litres   1 acre = 0·404 hectare)

Mr Edwin Bushby farms Watson Hill, Egremont, a farm of 127 acres, (51·4 hectares) and from his results it is clearly seen that he is a first-class operator. The herd benefits from many years of first-class management. His herd management, grassland management and silage-making are always excellent. This serves to show us what good management and good cows can do, and the figures of £331·8 margin over concentrates and a gross margin per cow and per acre of £295·9 are well worth remembering.

Table 17. Summary of Financial Results, Mr Edwin Bushby's, Watson Hill Farm, Egremont, Cumbria (March 1974–April 1975)

	Whole herd	Per cow
Average number of cows	122	—
Milk produced	169,150 gallons	1,387
Value of milk produced	£53,131	£434·6
Concentrates fed per cow	149 tons	24·4 cwt
Cost of concentrates	£13,761	£102·8
Margin over concentrates	£39,369	£331·8
Cost of fertiliser per acre	£22·00	£22·00
Forage acres used	122	
Concentrates used per gallon	2·00 lb	

Summary per acre and per cow (stocking rate 1·0 acre per cow).

Value of milk produced	£434·6
Value of calf	£24·6
Herd depreciation	minus £12·8
Total output	£446·4
Total variable costs	£150·5
GROSS MARGIN per acre	£295·9
GROSS MARGIN per cow	£295·9

(1 lb = 0·45 kg; 1 gallon = 4·54 litres; 1 acre = 0·405 hectare)

INDEX